# THE

# NEW WHIG GUIDE.

LONDON:

PRINTED FOR W. WRIGHT, 46, FLEET-STREET.

1819.

KRAUS REPRINT CO.
New York
1971

KRAUS REPRINT CO.
A U.S. Division of Kraus-Thomson Organization Limited

Printed in U.S.A.

# ADVERTISEMENT.

Political pasquinades and political carica-
tures are parts (though humble ones) of political
history: they supply information as to the personal
habits and manners, and often as to the motives
and objects of public men, which cannot be found
elsewhere.

It is true that the portraits are for the most
part exaggerated and unfavourable, but there is
still a general resemblance; and the ridicule, though
sometimes too highly coloured, is seldom wholly
unjust.

These pasquinades have usually appeared first
in the newspapers, and been subsequently collected into volumes; and though the Editor is far

from thinking that the articles he has here collected are of equal merit amongst themselves, or collectively to be compared with the Rolliad and Anti-jacobin, he yet considers them worth preserving, as filling up a space which would otherwise be vacant in the lighter history of parties in this country.

E.

# CONTENTS.

THE

# NEW WHIG GUIDE.

---

## THE CHOICE OF A LEADER.

### No. I.

*Feb.* 9, 1815.

THE Recess nearly spent, and approaching the hour,
That renews the vain struggle for places and power,
The Whigs, duly summon'd, are met to prepare
Their annual bill of political fare.


Their brows, like the season, are cloudy and dark ;
Of hope scarce a ray, and of joy not a spark
Illume any visage—save WHITBREAD's* alone,
Who grins as he fancies the game all his own,

* Samuel Whitbread, Esq., M. P. for Bedford.

B

Expects the whole sway of the faction to bear,
And sees his own strength in his party's despair.

And now to the meeting each member began
To open his separate project and plan,
And each in each varied event of the times
Beholds a new mark of the Ministry's crimes—
Bad faith with MURAT—and the low price of Corn,
The American Lakes—and the Duchy of Thorn,
The Legion of Honour—the trading in Blacks,
Baron IMBERT's arrest—and the Property Tax,
Colonel QUENTIN's Court-martial—and Spain's dis-
            content,
The Catholic claims—and the Treaty of Ghent ! *

For each sev'ral point, the proposer of each
Is duly equipp'd with a notice and speech;
While WHITBREAD, who seizes on every man's theme,
Like bold Bully Bottom, in Midsummer's Dream, †

---

* It seems from the parliamentary debates that all these were
subjects of discussion about this time.—E.

† Shakespeare's " Midsummer Night's Dream."

Would play every part, and proposes for all,
Duke, Pyramus, Thisbe, Moon, Lion, and Wall!

But while they prepared the defeat of their foes,
Within their own camp civil discord arose;
And, famish'd and gaunt, PADDY PONSONBY's * pack,
Like the hounds of Actæon, their huntsman attack.

" What boots our debate,"—thus the rebels began,
" What avails the discussion of topic or plan?
" No plan can succeed, and no party can thrive,
" With a leader who neither can lead us nor drive:
" Six Sessions of patience have witness'd our toil,
" Six Sessions of labour, not lighten'd by spoil;
" For six mortal years, as rhetorical graces
" We truisms cheer'd, and extoll'd common-places;
" Wash'd over with praise every folly and flaw,
" And smil'd at his jokes, and look'd grave at his law,

* The Right Honourable George Ponsonby, M. P. for Peterborough, the reputed leader of the opposition.—E.

" (Could friendship do more?) while indifferent folks

" All smil'd at his law, and look'd grave at his jokes.

" With patience we suffer'd in hopes he might mend,

" But patience and hope must at last have an end.

" Expect, then, to see half the party secede, or

" Provide us with some one more fit to be *leader*."


Applauses ensued ; and in shouts from the crowd

" New leader—new leader," is echoed aloud.

Less hoarse is the wave on the Hebridan shore,

Less loudly does MATHEW for Popery roar;

Less deep are the groans from the *Bar* that arise,

When NEWPORT begins on the Irish excise ;

Or when, as the candles burn dim in their sockets,

WILL SMITH rises up with both hands in his pockets ;

On a course of morality fearlessly enters,

And drawls all the twaddle of all the Dissenters.


But though to a change *all* appear to agree,

No two coincide who the leader should be ;

Each states his *own* merits—the prudent, the bold,
The grave and the light, and the hot and the cold;
The deep in finance, and the dextrous in wit,
Each fancies himself, for the office, most fit;
And, amidst ALL *the Talents*, would have it confess'd,
That his own little Talent is brightest and best.

At length 'tis proposed to allay all their grudges,
That GRENVILLE * and GREY † shall conjointly be
judges;
Unable their rancour a moment to smother,
The followers of neither will trust in the other.
Ambition, suspicion, self-love, and intrigue,
Are the cardinal points of this patriot league;
And lest the one worthy his brother should trick,
Like two Brentford kings, they must both hold the
stick,

* Lord Grenville, Secretary of State for Foreign Affairs in Mr.
Pitt's administration.—E.
† Lord Grey, Secretary of State for Foreign Affairs in Mr.
Fox's administration.—E.

And smell to one nosegay of sav'ry perfume,
Which the Whigs, too close pack'd, now exhale
         through the room.

The Chairmen thus named, proclamation is made;
(CHARLES WYNNE being Crier, with OSSULSTON's
         aid,) *
And the Meeting is strongly entreated to note
(The few who could speak, and the crowd who
         should vote ;)
As it was *not* the SPEAKER who now sat before 'em,
They ought to maintain *some* degree of decorum.

Then WHITBREAD arose (ever sure to be first
When Vanity's bubbles are going to burst) :
" Who dares," he began, " I repeat, who can *dare*
" *His* claims for this honour with *mine* to compare?
" My talents so various, my industry such,
" † I touch every theme, and adorn all I touch !

* The voices of these gentlemen are more than once alluded to
in other articles as being somewhat peculiar.—E.

† Nullum fere genus non tetigit, nullum quod tetigit non ornavit.

" Will any one promise, like me, to oppose

" All men and all measures, my friends and my foes?

" Like me, who can say, that he *never* was known

" To adopt or support any plan but his own?

" To the dictates of reason or feeling to bend?

" In short, who can say, that he ne'er had a friend?

" Have you eyes, have you ears, can you write, can

you read?

" And do you yet doubt who is fit to succeed?

" Did not BONAPART * make the *Moniteur* quote,

" With ample applause, both my words and my vote?

" And Denmark, enraged at her capital's breaches,

" In bitter state papers make use of my speeches?

" Do MADISON's journals not ring with my fame,

" And place next to JEMMY's your SAMUEL's name?

" Lo! MURAT the Great, (whom the Austrians fret,)

" Lauds WHITBREAD the Great in the Naples Gazette;

* It would seem that the admirers of Buonaparte affect to call
him by the *French* trisyllabic contraction of his name, while, elsewhere, the name is sounded as a quadrisyllable, agreeably to its
true Italian pronunciation.

" And in a *précis* of his foreign relations,

" Supplies me with matter for future orations.

" Magnanimous Monarch! in him I can see—

" Or fancy I can—some resemblance of me;

" In birth almost equal, in manners as bland,

" In temper as sweet, and as mild in command;

" As grateful, as modest—the blushes you view

" Forbid me the flattering theme to pursue;

" I give but a sketch—you who know me the best

" Will fill up the outline and colour the rest.

" Give *me* then the rank, which the wise and the
bold

" (Such as MURAT and I) are predestined to hold;

" And none but a fool or a knave can be jealous

" Of one, whom his merit exalts o'er his fellows.

" What though a few blockheads should grudge me
the meed,

" With scorn we shall see the deserters secede;

" *My rhet'ric* alone will suffice to your aid;

" And of *it* I may say, as we did to the trade

'' Of the prices of beer—(to detain you no longer)

" You can't have it *cheaper,* but shall have it

    * *stronger !*''

He said ; but no plaudit ensued—not a cheer!

Even CREEVEY † himself could not yelp out " Hear,

    Hear !''

And the judges pronounc'd—not a voice saying no—

That weak as they were, they had not run *so* low

In temper, in manners, in candour and birth,

To bow to this blustering " son of the earth ;" ‡

A bug-bear composed, like the idol of old,

Of *clay* and of *brass,* dizen'd over with gold !

---

 * This answer was made by Mr. Whitbread on a complaint of the increased prices of porter.—E.

 † Tho. Creevey, Esq. M. P. for Morpeth. He had been Secretary to the Board of Controul in the Talents' administration.—E.

 ‡ Terræ filius. A kind of general accuser, who at the Saturnalia of University commencements assumed a license of arraigning all mankind.

# THE CHOICE OF A LEADER.

## No. II.

*Feb.* 11, 1815.

THEN TIERNEY * arose : one might see that an air
Of candour and truth he *endeavour'd* to wear ;
But nature, too strong, gave his efforts the lie,
And the real expression was *tricky and sly.*

He began—very soberly stroking his chin—
" Although I should never have wish'd to begin
" This kind of discussion, yet since we are in it,
" With some plain remarks I'll detain you a minute.

" Let us see what is chiefly required in a Leader ?
" Not the fire of a bully, the phlegm of a pleader :
" Not a blusterer ' tearing a passion to rags ;'
" Not one who at nothing laboriously fags,

* George Tierney, Esq., M. P. for Appleby. Treasurer of the
Navy under Lord Sidmouth. President of the Board of Controul
with All the Talents.—E.

" But sound common sense, quiet, pliant, and cool;

" An address—which can work with a fact like a tool;

" A conscience—not qualmish, nor apt to grow sick;

" An art—as plain dealing to pass off a trick:

" To these, with a plausible manner and face,

" My scheme for a Leader assigns the first place.


" The next proposition I mean to advance

" Is this—that our chief should be skill'd in finance:

" Can one, not expert at financial debate,

" To any extent, clog the wheels of the State?

" What hope have we left but to bare to the axe

" That root of exertion the Property Tax?

" This done, a wise chief might proceed to assault

" The Excise and the Customs, the Land and the
Malt;

" And then it might be to the country revealed

" That taxes are needless, and should be repealed;

" And that, by disbanding the Army and Fleet,

" Economical Statesmen might make both ends meet.

" For my part, I'll vote for no leader alive

" Who cannot explain two and two to make five :

" What though he should have, for full twenty years
          past,\*

" Foretold that our credit no longer could last;

" What though, when his statements had led to
     suppose

" That Omnium would fall, it immediately rose;

" And on t'other hand, when he chanced to foretell

" That Omnium would rise, it immediately fell;

" What though, by confounded ill luck, 'twere de-
          creed,

" What he praises should fail—what he censures
     succeed :

" I repeat what I said, two and two should make five,

" And *finance* is the nail that is certain to drive !

---

\* The speaker here is made to describe what is supposed to be
his own parliamentary course. It cannot be denied that Mr.
Tierney has a great deal of good sense, and some arithmetical
knowledge; but his financial assertions have been generally dis-
proved both by figures and facts.—E.

" My third and last point I now hasten to state :

" No leader can properly guide a debate

" Unless, quite familiar with every one's views,

" He sees the whole game which each party pur-
sues ;

" And knows who are nibbling, who hungry, who
nice—

" The hope of each faction—and every man's price !

" These arts are not studied, like figures of speech,

" *Experience* alone such discretion can teach.

" To *lead*, then, believe me, a man you should call,

" All parties who knows—*having acted with all*,

" Has stood at their head, or has sneak'd at their tail,

" And all in the spirit of bargain and sale.

" I beg that the meeting will not understand,

" That I, for *myself*, have this object in hand ;

" I mean no such thing ; but my honest advice is,

" To try to select some *such* man at this crisis.

" Whomever it be—I have no private ends—

" I shall give, *as I always have done*, to my friends,

" Unbiassed by party, unswayed by the Court,
" A liberal, honest, and solid support."

Loud laughter ensued—such obstreperous mirth,
As Vulcan* in heaven or FLOOD † upon earth
Excite by their blunders—but GEORGE, unamazed,
Very readily join'd in the laugh he had raised,
And cried to his friends with satirical grin,
" Good folks, you may laugh—I'll be damn'd if you
win."

The judges then said that they never could vote
For one, who his party could change, like his coat;
And that, whosoever be chosen, he must,
At least, be a person that *some one* would trust.

* Iliad, b. 1.
† Sir F. Flood, Bart. M. P. for Wexfordshire, whose speeches
are generally accompanied in the reports with " *laughs*," " *laughing*," " *loud and continued laughter.*"    Vide Parliamentary Debates
passim.

# THE CHOICE OF A LEADER.

## No. III.

*Feb.* 20, 1815.

ALREADY (ere WHITBREAD or TIERNEY could close)
Brimful of a speech—on the tip of his toes—
With figure and visage so shrivel'd and weazen,
Already, *nine times*, little NEWPORT * had risen.

One often has seen Savoyards, at a fair,
Display the joint feats of a monkey and bear;
The bear dancing solemnly, while at his back
Sits wriggle-tail, mischievous, jabbering Jack;
Who, soon as old Bruin has finish'd his prance,
Starts up, in a twinkling, to chatter and dance.
And thus, of the party which we are reviewing,
Old NEWPORT is Jacko and WHITBREAD is Bruin.†

* Sir John Newport, Bart. M. P. for Waterford.—E.
† Quere, Brewing.

The speech Jacko utter'd, what pen can describe?
" Abuse—peculation—-corruption and bribe—
" Knave, jobber, and bigot—defaulter and rogue—"
Were the civilest words of his voluble brogue.
" The Meeting," he hoped, " would a leader elect,
" Whose courage and skill might such culprits detect;
" Whose zeal would not think it was going too far
" To summon some *thousands* of rogues to the bar;
" For him, he profess'd that he never would fail,
" To examine each case in the *greetest* detail :
" And that he already was furnish'd with plenty
" To last him 'till March eighteen hundred and
twenty.
" Would summon two Boards—the Excise and the
Stamps;
" Eight Post-office clerks—five contractors for
lamps—
" (Against the last mention'd he'd prove beyond
doubt
" At three in the morning, seven burners were out);

" The Lord Mayor of Dublin—who, as it is said,

" On the first of July wore an Orange cockade—

" A Weigher and Deputy-weigher at Cork,

" Who sunk half an ounce in one barrel of pork,

" And (scarcely his tongue his abhorrence could utter)

" Overcharg'd thirteen pounds in a cargo of butter.


" He also could shew, in direct violation

" Of law, that a peer in an eminent station

" Had brought to his Lady in this very town

" A remnant of poplin to make her a gown.


" He further could state, that in plain contraven-
     tion

" Of (if not the letter,) at least the intention

" Of that Act of Union so dear to us all,

" The Holyhead packets are vastly too small;—

" In blankets and basins but scantily found;—

" And charging a *Guinea* instead of a *Pound*.


c

" He pledged himself also to prove upon oath,
" (Though the facts were obscure, and the witnesses
       loth,)
" That a gauger, last winter, named TIMOTHY
       MILLER,
" Had accepted a dram from a Dublin distiller.


" He'd prove that a *Protestant* Justice of Peace
" Had wantonly seized a poor *Catholic*'s geese
" For arrears of his rent; though the fact would
       appear
" That the tenant was *barely three* years in arrear;
" And this very Justice, for reasons unknown,
" At midsummer fair of Maccollopmahone,
" Had dared to arrest a poor Popish Defendant,
" For stealing a *string*—with a pig at the end on't!"


At last, he concluded—" Abuses like these
" Are points which a Whig Opposition should seize :
" And *no* man unpractised in *Irish* debate
" Is fit to conduct the affairs of the State.

" And, as to the rest, I will dare to advance,

" Against even TIERNEY, my skill in finance;

" And WHITBREAD himself should acknowledge
　　my right,

" Who have spoken with ease *forty* times in one night;

" If any man doubts me, on this very floor,

" And this very day, I will speak forty more."


" We grant it—we grant it—there's no man can
　　doubt,

" You *could* talk till Christmas," was echoed about :

And the Judges, in fright, took no pains to conceal

They wanted no proof of his lungs or his zeal;

But said, that a leader should sometimes permit

The rest of the party to flourish a bit :

Should have, they declared, *some* attention to *fact*,

A spice of good-nature, some candour, some tact;

Their friends would scarce choose, for his talent and
　　rank,

The partner or clerk in a small country bank—

A short-sighted pedlar, proposing to prop
The State as he'd manage a cheesemonger's shop—
In short, though the party were at the last gasp,
They still would prefer the old *Drone* to a *Wasp.*

====

## THE CHOICE OF A LEADER.

### No. IV.

*March* 3, 1815.

Two Knights next arose to put forward their claims,
Sir SAMUEL* the solemn—the travell'd Sir JAMES ;†
Both Patriots bold, who with mighty applause
Stick up for Old England, her freedom and cause ;
Her *gold* in their pockets, her *law* in their brains,
'Twere well had they some of her *blood* in their veins.

* Sir S. Romilly, Knt. M. P. for Arundel, Solicitor-general under the Talents.

† Sir James Mackintosh, Knt. late Recorder of Bombay, M. P. for Nairn.

The first plainly bears the old *Genevese* print,
Lank person, sly feature, and chocolate tint;
While, strong, in the second, we see the " bra' bairn"
Who once tended swine in the County of Nairn.


'Twas pleasant to see with what efforts they tried
The powerful workings of Nature to hide;
'Twas pleasanter still to behold how, in spite
Of their efforts, old Nature would set herself right.


See ROMILLY leaning his head all awry,
His accent subdued, and submissive his eye,
His face, person, air, frozen up in restraint;
You think, the first glance, that the man is a saint;
And one would lament, as a very hard case,
That such a clear heart has so gloomy a face.
But when he is kindled, and passion has thaw'd
His ice, what dark spirits come prowling abroad!
Ambition, ill-temper, and turbulent pride,
Self-love, and disdain of all creatures beside;

You see and lament (through the mask of his art,)
That such a clear head has so gloomy a heart.


On t'other hand, MACKINTOSH strives to unite
The grave and the gay, the profound and polite :
And piques himself much that the ladies should say
How well Scottish strength softens down in Bombay;
Frequents the assembly, the supper, the ball,
The *philosophe-beau* of unloveable STAEL ; *
Affects to talk French in his hoarse Highland note,
And gargles Italian half way down his throat;
His gait is a shuffle, his smile is a leer,
His converse is quaint, his civility queer;
In short,—to all grace and deportment a rebel,—
At best, he is but a half-polish'd Scotch-pebble.


The Judges were doubtful on which first to call ;
Their names, in loud clamours, divided the hall;

* During Mad. de Stael's residence in England she was much
attended by Sir J. Mackintosh.—E.

At length, with a bow to the Genevese sage,
The Scottish Adonis relinquished the stage.


 Then Calvin's disciple began :—" I profess
" No wishes for power; no mortal has less;
" No man can be more unassuming and meek;
" With pain—real pain—I have risen to speak;
" But love of my kind overflows at my heart,
" And a deep sense of duty prescribes me my part.


 " Oh think to what crisis a country is come,
" Where justice is blind, and humanity dumb—
" Where under a barbarous system of laws
" (The good man's despair, and the blockhead's
   applause),
" An innocent debtor who happens to fail
" To take up his notes, may be cast into jail !
" And (worse than the savage who prowls in the
   woods)
" A tradesman expects to be paid for his goods !

" When a code unrelenting pronounces this curse,

" He pays with his *person,* who won't with his
purse *!*

" Where he, who a trifle shall steal in your *house,*

" Although he should make no more noise than a
mouse,

" Is doom'd by the law the same forfeit to pay

" As if he had taken it on the highway!

" Where the bravest and best of the nation, who
should

" *Mistake* the best road to the national good,

" For deeds, which a Roman would honour as great,

" Must lose, at a blow, both his life and estate:

" Because, by some *lex talionis,* 'tis shown

" Who risks those of others, should forfeit his own.

" O logic absurd! O condition most hard!

" That innocent babes of their rights should be
barr'd;

" And that his poor son, (if he so should aspire,)

" Has not the means left of avenging his sire!

" Where, in short, all the laws against thieving or
  treason
" Are shocking to policy, feeling, and reason!


" Thus, thus 'tis the *law* that ensanguines the
  times;
" The *law* is the source of these horrors and crimes;
" What, tho' its foundations by ALFRED were laid—
" Tho' farther advanced by the Confessor's aid—
" Tho' towards its perfection the Norman concurr'd—
" Tho' extorted from JOHN at the point of the
  sword—
" Tho' thro' a long series of ages, the law
" At once kept the monarch and people in awe—
" And though that long series of ages confess'd
" The monarchs were great, and the people were
  blest—
" Tho' in our own days we have seen all mankind,
" To philosophy deaf, and to theory blind,
" Both monarchs and people combining their powers,
" To build up *their* laws on the model of *ours*—

" Notwithstanding all this—I assert, on the word

" Of a saint and a sage, that the law is absurd !

" And, tho' some dull bigot my ears may assail

" With COKE, and with BLACKSTONE, with FOSTER,
            and HALE,

" YORKE, CAMDEN or MANSFIELD—I have to con-
            front 'em,

" MONTESQUIOU, BECCARIA, and JEREMY BENTHAM.


" Let *me* then be leader; place me in the van,

" To work out the moral perfection of man;

" The halter, the axe, I'll dismiss in a trice,

" And substitute for them good *wholesome advice;*

" All causes by ethical dogmas determine,

" Without the vain form of the Coif and the Er-
            mine;

" The Judges a felon with *proverbs* shall trounce,

" And *sermons* instead of a *sentence* pronounce;

" Manufactories then, on a liberal scale,

" Shall serve every purpose of bridewell and jail;

" And, saved to his country, the criminal wretch

" Shall then *pound* the hemp he at present would

stretch.


" Then *real* estates,—held so sacred of old,—

" For payment of *personal* debts should be sold;

" And generous heirs, too impatient to wait,

" Might lose, ere they had it, their father's estate;

" Young RUSSELS and HOWARDS, by mere note of

hand,

" Would then parcel out all their family land;

" And fathers themselves, if a wine-merchant's bill

" Grew pressing, would slice off a manor at will,

" And thus we should see in a fortunate hour

" An equal division of wealth and of power."


He ended—and MARTIN,* just wak'd from a doze,

Grew conscious, and snuffled applause through his

nose;

* Henry Martin, Esq., Barrister at Law, M. P. for Kinsale. See page 42.

The Judges, however, pronounced their belief
(Howe'er he might deal with the traitor and thief,)
It would not, just then, be expedient to force
The great stream of property out of its course,
Or that, for example, the person who gets
Lord Camelford's land * should be charged with his
                    debts;
Such visions and dreams might pass off in a pleader,
But never would suit a political *leader*.
And that as to law and religion, the Nation
Abhorr'd *foreign* projects and rash innovation;
And ne'er would consent their palladium to see
In the hands of the Son of a French Refugee.


* Lord Grenville succeeded to the late Lord Camelford's real
estates.—E.

# THE CHOICE OF A LEADER.

## No. V.

*March 6, 1815.*

WITH clumsy alacrity MACKINTOSH rose,
Removed his old hat from the bridge of his nose,
Uncover'd his eyes to the light of the day,
And show'd his dark locks lightly sprinkled with
  grey—
Those *patriot* locks, which at liberty roam,
Untarnish'd with powder, untamed by the comb;
Which, wild and erect on his forehead, are seen,
True types of the freedom that harbours within.

He spoke, but to copy his idiom and tones
The muse her despair very candidly owns;—
The sound was as Virgil describes of the croak
Of ravens, that sit on the sinister oak,—

The language, where flourish and flimsiness join,
Resembles good English, as counters do coin.


" With ample respect for the erudite, great,
" And eminent men who adorn this debate,
" With deference deep and profound to the chair,
" Or rather to those whom I see sitting there,
" I humbly beg leave to express my surprise
" On a question so plain how a doubt can arise;
" And that it should not be allowed on all hands
" What views and what talents the crisis demands.


" Is this a fit season our notice to draw
" To quiddits and quirks of the Old Bailey law ;
" The rise of a duty, the fall of a loan ;
" Or drunken affrays of Maccollopmahone ?
" When Europe (I love great examples to quote)
" Is like the head dish at a Spa *table d'hote ;*
" Where men of all nations, with stomachs not nice,
" Are anxious to seize the best spoonful and slice.

" When tyrants are basely colleaguing to trench

" On the rights of that innocent people the French ;

" I gave to their efforts in Liberty's cause

" My first and shall still give my latest applause;

" You all must remember my earliest work,

" To *vindicate Gaul* * from the slanders of BURKE ;

" I ventured the banners of freedom to wave

" In the face of that pensioner, bigot, and slave ;

" And, sanguine in hope, with sublime elocution,

" Applauded the march of the French Revolution ;

" Defended—of mortals the wisest and best—

" MIRABEAU, CONDORCET, PETION, and the rest,

" By whose active minds and stout hands were o'er-
thrown

" Of priestcraft the altars—of despots the throne—

" Precursors and guides in their brilliant career,

" Of HE'BERT, MARAT, and the great ROBES-

" PIERRE—

* Vindiciæ Gallicæ, by James Mackintosh.—E.

" We saw, by their efforts, the limits of France

" In rapid progression o'er Europe advance,

" Before her, Kings, Princes, and Commonwealths
                " fall

" On the Po, the Tessino, the Rhine and the Waal!

" And who can behold, without sorrow and pain,

" This flourishing Empire *dismember'd* again?

" Her standards repell'd from the Sarre and the
            Dyle,

" All the way to the out-works of Verdun and Lille :

" The friends of political freedom will mourn

" On *this* side the Rhine to see Germans return;

" And, even the cruelest heart it must touch,

" That Holland is basely transferr'd to the Dutch!


" But this is not all—the complaints of the Poles

" Should ring in our ears, and sink deep in our
            souls!

" That nation, once happy, *united*, and free,

" Near forty years since was divided in three!

" Before that atrocious event, 'tis confest,

" No people was ever more *tranquil*, more blest;

" Except once a year, when a question might rise

" Between two great parties—the *sko's* and the *ski's,*

" And diets and councils of state came to blows

" To determine the claims of the *ski's* and the *sko's.*

" And shall not Great Britain (of justice the pattern)

" Redress the oppressions of FRED'RICK and CATH'-
 RINE!

" And reclaim, for the Poles, by our voices and votes,

" Their national birth-right—to cut their own
 throats?


" But scarcely less vile than the seizure of Poland

" Has been our base conduct to poor Heligoland;

" That innocent isle we have stolen from the Danes,

" And it groans with the weight of our trade and
 our chains.

" On that happy strand, not two lustres ago,

" The thistle was free in luxuriance to grow;

D

" The people at liberty starv'd, and enjoy'd

" Their natural freedom, by riches uncloy'd.

" But, now, all this primitive virtue is fled;

" Rum, sugar, tobacco, are come in its stead ;

" And, debauch'd by our profligate commerce, we
        see

" This much-injur'd race drinking porter and tea,

" And damning, half-fuddled (I tell it with pain)

" Their true and legitimate master—the Dane !


" The Dane !—Oh what thoughts at that word
        must arise !

" A Monarch so good, unambitious and wise ;

" Who firm and devoted by BONAPART stood,

" And ne'er injured England—except when he could !

" Yet this worthy Prince, we, by treaties, despoil

" At first of his ships, and at length of his soil.


" Akin to this crime, are the allied attacks on

" The royal, revered, and respectable Saxon !

" Good heav'ns, with what colours, what words
>> can I paint
" The trials and woes of this suffering saint!
" At Dresden so bold, and at Leipsic so true,
" To the aid of the French all his forces he drew,
" And, from their united success he afar saw
" A richer reward than the Duchy of Warsaw.
" Had fortune not frown'd on NAPOLEON the Great,
" How different, to-day, were AUGUSTUS's fate!
" The Niemen, the Rhine, then, had bounded his
>> reign,
" And Stralsund displayed his gay flag o'er the main;
" In Prague he, perhaps, had exalted his seat,
" And Hamburgh and Dantzig had crouch'd at his
>> feet;
" Then Prussia's proud King (if the French spared
>> his head)
" Had begged through the world for a morsel of bread,
" And the Elbe and the Danube, the Oder and Weser,
" Had giv'n to *Augustus* the title of *Cæsar*.

" Though Germany, England, France, Sweden
        and Spain,
" Russia, Prussia, and Portugal join to maintain
" These crimes, I assert, without fear of receding,
" *Unanimous* EUROPE condemns the proceeding ;—
" I have lately in Switzerland been, and declare
" The *crowds* which I met in the *solitudes* there,
" Men, women, and children, the goatherds, and
        goats—."

But here a loud laugh quell'd the orator's notes ;
And glad to extinguish a preacher so dull,
The Meeting unanimous bellowed " a bull !!"
Save MATHEW alone, who, in accents of thunder
And great indignation, roar'd out "a *Scotch blunder!*"

In vain poor Sir JAMES, in a treble-pitch'd screech,
Endeavour'd to follow the thread of his speech ;
Coughs, sneezes, and laughs, pealing loud thro' the
        room,
Pronounc'd, in a tempest, the candidate's doom ;

And ev'n of the Judges' decision no more
Than a word here and there could be heard in the roar,
As—" SIDMOUTH * "—" apostate"—" suspicion"—
" not clear"—
" Vindiciæ"—" BURKE"—" pension"—" two thou-
sand a year"—
" Scot"—" both sides"—" best bidder"—" though
never so clever"—
" A Jacobin once, and a Jacobin ever"!!! †


\* Lord Sidmouth had in his administration made Mr. Mackintosh Recorder of Bombay.—E.

† This series does not seem to have been brought to its intended
conclusion : the editor however has searched all the subsequent
journal of the year, but has found nothing more of this kind.—E.

# THE OPPOSITION.

*April* 14, 1815.

WE have been favoured with the following original, though we think rather favourable and partial
observations, on the Opposition Members of the
House of Commons, by a very respectable native of
the United States, a Quaker, of Pensylvania.   They
are contained in a letter, very recently written, to a
friend in America, a leading Member of the Government, a copy of which we are permitted to publish
for the amusement of our readers.

**TO MR. TOBIAS BRANDE, OF BIGMUDDY, MARYLAND,
UNITED STATES.**

" No. 5, Bearbinder-lane,
the 3d day of the 4th month.

FRIEND TOBIAS,—Thou hast oftentimes en-
joined me to send thee some particulars concerning
the persons who are called the Opposition in this

country, and whom thou rightly considerest as better friends to the States than any federalist between Blowing-Fly-Creek and Passamaquoddy Bay. That I may be the better enabled to comply with thy injunctions, I have posted myself from day to day in the gallery of the Parliament House, and have collected by inquiries from others, and my own observation, much curious information, of which I will now, God willing, impart to thee a portion.

Thou first inquirest what are the numbers of the Opposition : of this matter I cannot tell thee more, than that I have seen their numbers vary from three to twenty-three or thereabouts. On the very last night I was there, their muster-roll was the strongest, amounting to twenty-one in a lump or compact body, and some two or three stragglers at the bar.

As for their persons and appearance, which thou requirest me to describe, it may suffice that I tell thee that they very much resemble an equal number of Members of Congress. Thou wouldst say that I spoke from prejudice and partial affection, if I were to affirm what doth nevertheless appear to me—that on the whole they were not quite so well favoured.

They call a short and squattish Gentleman of the name of Ponsonby, their Leader—but my mind misgives me if there be not more than one half who are loth to follow him. The leader is, as verily he ought to be, a very cautious guide, and rarely propoundeth he any thing which can be contradicted or objected to. There is so much sameness and discretion in his style, that I can enable thee to judge of any quantity of it by a small sample. Discoursing of a treaty of peace, quoth the Leader—' I cannot pronounce an opinion upon this treaty, Mr. Speaker, until I have read it. No one has a right, Mr. Speaker, to call on me for an opinion upon this treaty until I have read it. This treaty cannot be printed, and in the hands of Members before Tuesday next at noon—and then, and not until then, Mr.

Speaker, will I, for one, form my opinion—upon this treaty. I am not such a fool as I am generally supposed to be.' Here he pauseth, and raising his spectacles with his hand, and poising them dexterously on his forehead, he looketh steadily at the Speaker for some moments.

Whitbread (not Whitebread, as thou callest him) hath more weight, I think, than the Leader. He is a very boisterous and lengthy speaker, and strongly remindeth me of Bully Pycroft of Kentucky, whom thou knowest, though he is inferior to Pycroft in taste and elegance.

There is a man of the name of Tierney, one not of many words, but who appeareth to me mighty shrewd and sensible. ' I will wager a dollar that that is an honest man,' said I, one evening, to my neighbours in the gallery; upon which they all cried ' done,' and laughed very heartily : I know not why.

These three, together with a small Baronet from Ireland, of a most cantanckerous turn ; and a

Member * from Scotland chiefly remarkable for his silken small-clothes and hose, call they ' the *great guns.*'

I will now speak to thee of some of the smaller fry, who, nevertheless, consider themselves just as big as their betters, and walk up to their seats in the Parliament House with huge bundles of papers under their arms, with great solemnity.

I must first tell thee of my friend, Mr. Will †
Martin, with whom I have formed an acquaintance, and in whose company I take great delight. I dined with him at the chophouse last Wednesday, and, to say the truth, found him a man after my own kidney. As a public speaker, he is chiefly noticed for a strange

---

* Probably Sir J. Mackintosh, whose costume is sometimes singular.—E.

† This gentleman, though he is all through these papers called *Will* Martin, seems to be Henry Martin, Esq. M. P. for Kinsale : the reason of the nickname of *Will* does not appear. Mr. Martin is a Barrister at Law, and it seems, from the article of Sporting Intelligence, (p. 59.) to be a professional allusion.—E.

habit, that whenever he openeth his mouth, he taketh that opportunity of closing his eyes.

There is one Mr. Gordon,* a middle-aged gentleman with a grave visage, who hath an appropriate but unseemly cognomen, which, as thou wilt probably shew my letter to thy wife, I will impart to thee in a Postscript.

I must not forget a dainty young gentleman of the name of Lambton,† who declaimeth in a very peculiar style. I know not whether there be more of oil in his deportment, or of vinegar in his tongue. I must indulge thee from my memorandum book with a specimen of this youth. Speaking one day of the Congress and the Kings at Vienna, saith he—

' What, Sir! shall a club of congregated cannibals
' feed on the carcasses of unoffending Europe ?
' What, Sir! shall his Majesty's Ministers, a set of

---

* Robert Gordon, Esq. M. P. for Wareham : from the Sporting Intelligence, (p. 59.) and from one of the English Melodies, (p. 121.) this *unseemly cognomen* may be guessed. This it is presumed is the reason that this gentleman is called Mr. *B.* Gordon.—E.

† M. P. for Durham.

' profligate and perjured swindlers, retain their seats
' in the Cabinet when they ought to be drawn and
' quartered without a trial! As for Lord Castlereagh,
' Sir, I thank my God three times a day that the
' noble and unsullied blood of the Lambtons is not
' polluted by any admixture with that of the plebeian
' Stewarts.' Thou must admit that these are hard
words, and yet delivered he them with so much
composure and good-humour, and to all outward
appearance so little moved was he by the spirit, that
I conjecture he was by no means in earnest, but per-
chance a secret partisan of the Ministry: the more
so as Mr. Chancellor Vansittart * thrice said ' *Hear,
Hear !*' during his declamation; and Friend Martin
whispered me, ' that the jackanapes,' as merrily he
called him, ' did his own party more harm than good.'

There is also a Mr. I. Grant, † a swaggering
man, but in my mind a vapid speaker. He seemeth

---

* The Chancellor of the Exchequer seems to be liberal of his
ejaculatory approbation to his opponents.—E.

† J. P. Grant, Esq. M. P. for Grimsby; a Scottish barrister.

well contented with himself, but on this and other matters holding strange doctrines, wherein he standeth alone.

I have heard many questions put very genteelly by a Mr. Bennet,\* an *honourable;* who is in my mind mighty well bred, though he disfigureth himself by wearing a green wig. He is attentive to business, and hath lately discovered a mistake of three farthings in an account of thirty millions: but he somewhat surprised me by calling the Secretary at War (*the Munro* of this Country,) his *honourable friend* and a *very infamous man*, in the same breath.

He hath a brother † elder in years but less in sta-

\* The Honourable Henry Grey Bennet, M. P. for Shrewsbury. At Eton he was sometimes called ' Bennet with a *green baize wig*,' and sometimes ' *frothy* Bennet:' the reason of the former name, which is alluded to in the text, I cannot explain; the latter is obvious enough. These names are frequently alluded to in subsequent articles.—E.

† Lord Ossulston, M. P. for Knaresborough. His Lordship was Comptroller of the Household to his Majesty during the Talents' administration; an office of little or no importance. It is reported

ture than himself, who rarely speaketh, the which I attribute to his having held an important office of the State, which hath taught him to be wise and keep silence. I know not more of his office, than that the insignia thereof consisted of a staff or stick many feet longer than him who bore it.

I must not forget the mention of Sir Charles Monck,* whom I reckon a merry and facetious jester. He hath kept the whole House in a state of merriment upwards of three quarters of an hour, by reading an ancient missal respecting something which he called the Order of the Bath. He was, however, despite of his jests, grievously disposed to blame an addition of forty marks to the salary of a deputy messenger, which he said was a violation of the Consti-

of him, that the mode of his dismissal was the sovereign's taking the white staff out of his hand, and putting it on the mantle-piece of the closet out of his reach.—E.

* Sir C. Monck, M. P. for Northumberland, appears about this time to have made a motion relative to the new regulation of the order of the Bath, notice of which had been given (as it seems from these papers) by Mr. Robert Gordon.—E.

tution, and a discharge of the subjects of the realm from their allegiance; and such is the wretched state of the finances of this country, that this worthy Country Member protested he did not know where the forty marks were to come from.

Lastly, let me name to thee a youngster, who hath been mistaken for a wit in foreign parts, by the name of North Douglas.*—He seemeth to belong to no party, and yet willing to belong to all. He is a forward and frequent speaker—remarkable for a graceful inclination of the upper part of his body, in advance of the lower, and speaketh, I suspect, (after the manner of an ancient) with pebbles in his mouth. He hath a strange custom, when speaking, of holding his hat in one hand, and smoothing the felt of it with the other, the which made me at the

* The Honourable Frederick North Douglas, son of Lord Glenbervie, M. P. for Banbury. It would seem that the fourth Melody, p. 126, alludes to this Gentleman, who seems by the parliamentary debates to have voted with the Administration the first half of the Parliament, and with the Opposition the second.—E.

first entertain a ludicrous notion that he was recommending the hat to the Speaker, and exhorting him to purchase it.

I must now bid thee farewel, but I have much more to communicate to thee.

Thy Friend,

EZEKIAL GRUBB.

———

# SECOND LETTER

**FROM MR. EZEKIAL GRUBB TO MR. TOBIAS BRANDE**

**OF BIGMUDDY.**

5, Bearbinder-lane,
10th day of 5th month.

WORTHY TOBIAS,—In my last I expounded unto thee, with what skill I could command, the characters of most of the persons in the Parliament House, who go by the name of the Opposition—insomuch that I have little more at this present writing to impart to thee on that head.

It seemeth good that I should now present unto thee some information regarding the nature of the business upon which the said Parliament House and the Members thereof are ordinarily engaged. Upon the table of the House there lieth a sort of ledger or entry book, in the which a Member purposing to propound any matter inscribeth it beforehand, that due notice may be had thereof. By the favour of Martin, I have procured a sight of this valuable register or record; and shall, for the better edification and induction into the mysteries of the legislation of this people, indulge thee with certain transcripts thereof. And let me first premise unto thee, that in many cases the precise nature of the business is not easily to be comprehended (by a stranger at least) from the entry thereof in the book.

E

Nor can I well translate unto thee what is signified by such terms as these : " *Scotch Hawkers bill, 2d time ;*"—" *Co. Sugar Mistake bill ;*"—"*Irish Vermin, 3d time ;*"—" *Madder explanation bill, Rep. ;*"— " *British White Herring bill Co.*"——In most cases, however, the entry is sufficiently clear to shew to thee the object of the *mover*, as he is called, because when he riseth to speak he putteth himself into a great deal of motion, and generally also moveth several Members to depart ; and by frequent attention to the purport of the notices each man giveth, thou mayest judge of his capacity and public conduct. From this entry-book I surmise that there is not a man who hath more real business to transact than the little Irishman, of whom I spoke in my last, and who is so well respected by both parties that he is commonly called the *worthy* Baronet ; wherein his worthiness above his fellows consists I have not satisfied myself, but suspect it is his great good humour and pleasant temper. He hath at the present time 33 entries or notices on the book, and of the great moment thereof to the State thou mayest judge for thyself from the following examples:—

" Notice.—Tuesday, May 23.

" Sir John Newport—To move for a Copy of the Commission of Thady Doyle, a supernumerary gauger; and a Copy of all Correspondence between the Excise Board in Ireland and any supernumerary gauger, on the subject of the illicit distillation of aniseed water, since the Union with this country."

" Ditto—To refer for the opinion of the twelve Judges the Petition of Michael Kenny, of the city of Waterford, merchant and huckster, complaining of a surcharge of 3s. 9½d. Irish currency."

" Wednesday, May 24.

" Ditto—Bill to abolish the Office of Crier of the Justiciary Court of Scotland, and to carry the net emolument of the said Office to the account of the Commissioners for Draining the Bog of Allen."

" Thursday, May 25.

" Ditto—To appoint a Commission under the Sign Manual, to inquire whether the Isle of Man is, according to the Articles of Union, a part of Ireland or of Great Britain; and to move for a return of the duties on wrought plate and jewels, imported from the said Island into the port of London, in the last year."

I shall now proceed with a transcript of divers other motions and notices, likewise of great im-

E 2

portance, and very praiseworthy in the gentlemen who introduce the same:

" MR. PETER MOORE—An Act to abolish the River Thames, and to substitute instead thereof a canal from Staines to Sheerness, to be called the Royal Clarence Canal." *

" *Thursday, Feb.* 2.

" LORD NUGENT—Motion for the production of all the Logs of H. M. packets *Montague* and *Pelham,* since they were launched."

" *Friday, March* 17.

" *Ditto*—To appoint a committee to inspect all mail bags which may have been conveyed in H. M. packets *Montague* and *Pelham,* in the years 1809, 1810, 1811, 1812, and 1813."

" *Saturday, April* 1.

" *Ditto*—To address H. R. H. the Prince Regent that he will be pleased to appoint Timothy Perring, Esq. late Commander of the *Lady Pelham* packet, Commander-in-chief of the Channel Fleet."

" *Wednesday, May* 31.

" *Ditto*—In Supply, to move a sum of 4,365*l.* 7*s.* 8¾*d.* towards defraying the expenses of printing the papers relative to the *Montague* and *Pelham* packets. Also,—to move for an account of the number of purser's lanterns supplied to each of H. M. ships or vessels employed on the Halifax, East India, Downs, and other foreign stations."

* Incredible as it may seem, there was a bill of this or a somewhat similar nature introduced by Mr. Moore.—E.

" GENERAL THORNTON—Bill to compel hackney and other coachmen to be more civil towards female passengers; and likewise to amend the acts relating to the uniformity of the Common Prayer."

"MR. BENNET—Move for leave to bring in a bill to regulate the office of necessary woman to the state apartments at St. James's."

" MR. BARHAM—Bill to make it felony, without benefit of clergy, to intermarry with the descendants of persons carrying on, or related to persons carrying on, the Slave Trade."

" MR. WM. SMITH—Move for leave to bring in a bill to amend the Doctrine of the Trinity."

" MR. M. A. TAYLOR—Bill to regulate the size of paviors, and to prevent parish vestries from employing such men, below a certain stature." *

" Ditto—To abolish the punishment of the stocks; and to provide that all stocks built or building at the passing of the act shall be deemed to be old naval stores, and disposed of as such."

" MR. GORDON—Motion for a repeal of the Alien Act, and for an address to his Royal Highness the Prince Regent, praying that H. R. H. will be graciously pleased to inform the House by whose advice a Hottentot Lady, of the name of Sartjee,† has been removed from this country."

" MR. COKE—Motion for leave to bring in a bill to abolish all existing duties of Customs and Excise, and to exempt all persons

* Mr. Michael Angelo Taylor has been designated as a " pocket Hercules."

† A Hottentot woman was about this time exhibited in London, possessing in a remarkable degree the peculiar protuberance for which her species is noted.—E.

having landed property to the amount of 20,000*l.* per annum, and upwards, from the payment of the Property Tax."

"*Ditto*—Bill to prevent the Crown from declaring war without the consent of Grand Juries of the several counties."

I was somewhat surprised to see so little mention made in this book of the great lawyer Romilly, of whom thou hast heard Gallatin * speak with much applause—but Martin, who is a great admirer of Sir Samuel's, (and for good reason, as he liveth next door to him, and thus getteth some law business, which the other is so friendly as to refuse for his sake,) pointed out to me in the book of a former year, of which he obtained me the sight, several attempts in which Romilly unhappily failed, of ridding the Statute Book of all laws of great age and undue severity, and of making in lieu thereof more easy and convenient laws of his own. From this book I will send thee some extracts, sufficient to prove to thee the wisdom and merciful disposition

* M. Gallatin is a Swiss by birth, and Sir S. Romilly is said to be of Swiss extraction.—E.

of this *eminent person*, which is the name by which he calleth himself, and which his friends delight to repeat.

" SIR SAMUEL ROMILLY—Bill to repeal the existing laws in regard to high treason—and to provide that all persons compassing the death of the King in future shall be guilty of petty larceny, fined five pounds, and imprisoned for a time not exceeding two calendar months."

" *Ditto*—Bill to repeal so much of a Law of William the Conqueror as provides, that if an Archbishop or Bishop kills any of the King's Deer, without first blowing a horn, that he may not seem to steal the same—he shall be amerced of life or limb—at the discretion of the Court."

" *Ditto*—Move to repeal an Act passed in the 29th year of Henry VI. chap. 1, for the attainting Jack Cade of High Treason —and for the corrupting of his blood."

" *Ditto*—Leave to bring in a Bill to mitigate the penalties imposed by an Act passed in the reign of Edward IVth, on persons playing at the games of Klosse—Half-bowle—Kayles— Hand-in-hand—or Queckborn."

" *Ditto*—Leave to bring in a Bill to amend an Act of the 19th year of Henry VII. chap. 6, for punishing with death all Priests, and religious men convicted of fornication or other fleshy incontinence." *

* There are really statutes with these titles; and indeed many of the preceding notices are to be found, with little variation, in the debates of the period.—E.

Notwithstanding it was admitted on all hands that these ancient laws were never enforced, yet strange to say, the House preferred them and the old Code to the new one, which Sir Samuel had prepared.

I say nothing to thee of the entries made on the behalf of Whitbread, because as they are of a marvellous great number, he requireth a larger share of my letter than I can at present afford, seeing that I have now to speak to thee of the business of the tobacco and cotton, consigned by thee unto my care, under the favour of Baring, Brothers, and Co.; but inasmuch as thou mayest choose, in performance of thy duty as a good citizen, to impart these my political speculations unto Mr. Munroe, thou mayest not be willing at the same time to reveal the particulars of thy commercial concerns, I shall talk to thee of these matters in a separate sheet of paper. In the meanwhile, in truth and the spirit, I remain thy loving friend,        EZEKIAL GRUBB.

*P. S.* I am minded to leave this great Babylon

for a few days, being bidden by my worthy friend, (who hath taken off much of thy last parcels of Sea-Islands), Geo. Phillips, Esq. and M. P. to solace myself with a visit to his manufactory at Manchester, which, as my soul, after so long a sojourn in this town, yearneth after pure air and quiet,* I purpose, God willing, to do; and shall proceed with Mr. Phillips, the morning after the morrow, in the three-day coach.

* In some debates on cotton manufactories, Mr. Phillips stated that his manufactory was *more* healthy in proportion to the number of its inhabitants than any ordinary residences.—E.

## SPORTING EXTRAORDINARY.

*April* 11, 1815.

WE understand that the most distinguished Members of Opposition, weary of exertions so little successful as their parliamentary labours, and mutually dissatisfied with politics and each other, have, in imitation of Sir F. BURDETT, taken to rural sports, and have subscribed for a Sweepstakes, to be run for next month at Holkham.* The following is a list of the horses at present entered :—

Mr. WHITBREAD's *Rant-away,* by *Arrogant* out of *Quassia.*

Mr. TIERNEY's *Silvertail,* by *Jack-o'both-sides* out of *Slyboots.*

Mr. PONSONBY's *Leader,* by *Flounderer* out of *No-Conjurer.*

---

* The seat of Tho. Coke, Esq. in Norfolk, where there are generally annual meetings of the Members of the Opposition who are fond of sporting or agriculture.—E.

Sir S. ROMILLY's *Scorpion,* by *Watchmaker* out of *Hypocrite.*

Mr. MARTIN's *Goldfinder,* by *Attorney* out of *Legacy.*

Mr. GORDON's *Bumpkin,* by *Bumfiddle* out of *Breechiana.*

Mr. BENNETT's *Froth,*\* by *Drummer-boy* out of *Baywig.*

Mr. GRANT's *Patch,* by *My Eyes!* out of *Betty Martin.*

Mr. LAMBTON's *Conceit,* by *Memory* out of *Looking-glass.*

Sir J. NEWPORT's *Wasp,* by *Saucy Jack* out of *Kate Karney.*

Mr. HORNER's *Reformer,* by *Presbyterian,* out of *Jacobin.*

Sir F. FLOOD's *Looney Mactwolter,* by the *Podereen Mare* † out of *Potatoes.*

\* See p. 45.

† There appears to be a mistake of the sexes of the horses, or at least an inversion of their names; but we copy the list as given in by the worthy owner.

## POLITICAL BOTANY.

1815.

We have been favoured with a specimen of an ingenious attempt to improve the arrangement of the Red Book on scientific principles, and to introduce the Linnean system into the Parliamentary register.

The following Botanical Classification of certain eminent political characters, who frequent *Kew*'s Chop-room in the House of Commons, will be acceptable, we presume, both to politicians and botanists.

HORTUS KEWENSIS.

CLASSIS.—Polyandria Monogynia.

GENUS.—Alopecurus—FOX-TAIL.

SPECIES.—Communis—the Commons.

Individuals.

1. *Vulgaris*      -      Whitbread.

2. *Trivialis*      -      Ponsonby.

| 3. *Spinosissimus* | - | Newport. |
| 4. *Monopticon* | - | Grant. |
| 5. *Tauricum* | - | Flood. |
| 6. *Arachnoides* | - | Freemantle. |
| 7. *Americanus* | - | Baring. |
| 8. *Tortuosus* | - - | Tierney. |
| 9. *Rubicundus* | - | Barham. |
| 10. *Somnifer* | - | Hippisley. |
| 11. *Nanus Grandiflorus* | | Taylor. |
| 12. *Crista-galli* | - - | Lambton. |
| 13. *Anserinus* | - | Martin. |

# THE COUNTESS OF JERSEY'S MASQUERADE.

April 22, 1815.

On Wednesday evening the above distinguished Lady opened her magnificent residence in Berkeley-square, to the fashionable world. The entertainment consisted of a Masqued Ball followed by a Supper, and was attended by the whole of that exalted circle in which her Ladyship moves. The superb suite of apartments were brilliantly illuminated, and the richest wines, and most costly viands, did the greatest credit to the care of Mr. Gunter. We never witnessed a richer display of wit and humour than the Masquerade afforded, and we have only to regret that our limits will permit us to take notice of a few only of the principal guests.

His Royal Highness the Duke of *Sussex*, as *Pat-*

*Riot*, an *Irish Chairman*, exhibited all his usual grace and dignity.

His Highness the Duke of *Glocester*, as a *Milk-maid*, was simple and natural, and distributed her curds and whey with great affability.

We observed none of the Foreign Ministers, except the Ambassadors from Saxony, King Murat, and the Spanish Insurgents : their Excellencies assumed no character, but continued masked the whole evening. Mr. *Pig-blank*,\* late Professor of Hebrew in the University of Salamanca, and Envoy from the Cortes of Spain to the Whig Club, was also present, and his Excellency speaking no language but Spanish and Hebrew, Mr. *Whitbread* accompanied him for a part of the evening as interpreter ; but as Mr. *Whitbread* speaks no language but English, the conversation was somewhat constrained, and we lost a good

---

\* There was at this time in England a Spanish exile of the name of Puigblanch, who received some countenance from Mr. Whitbread, who mentioned his case in parliament.—E.

deal of Mr. *Pig-blank's* pleasantry.—The remainder
of the night Mr. W., as *Bully Bottom,** kept the
room in a roar, he wore his ass's ears with great
impudence and effect, and on the whole was the
best representative we have seen of the pert, ignorant, vulgar, swaggering, and sneaking bully of
our immortal bard.

Lord *Grenville* and Earl *Grey*, as the *Coachman*
and *Guard* of an *Opposition* diligence just overturned,
by coming in contact with a waggon laden with
corn,† were much followed—The sulky growl of
Coachee was well contrasted with the lively rage of
the Guard; and their mutual complaints of the im-
proper disposition of the passengers, and their lug-
gage, the rate of driving, the blindness of one of the
leaders, and the lameness of the other, were carried
on with a great deal of truth and fury.

* See page 2.
† An allusion probably to the *Corn Bill.*—E.

Mr. *Tierney*, as *Harlequin*, was certainly deficient in corporeal activity ; but he made ample amends for that defect by the variety of his shifts, and the rapidity of his transformations ; the best of which, we think, was a scene in which Harlequin disguised himself as a Quaker, and put on an air of plausibility, bluntness, and honesty, which might have deceived a sharper eye than that of the Clown, who was represented, with great fidelity and lumpishness, by *Sir W. Geary.** 

The *Marquis Wellesley*, as a Mountebank, and Mr. *Commissioner Sydenham*,† as his man, were perhaps the most natural characters in the room—the finical gravity and empty pretensions with which

* M. P. for Kent.

† B. Sydenham, Esq. a Commissioner of Excise, was supposed to have written a series of letters under the signature of Vetus, remarkable for their inflated panegyrics upon the Marquis Wellesley. It was afterwards said that Mr. S. was not the *writer*, but the *procurer* of this flattery, and the Editor has heard from other authority that he was *neither*. It is now of little consequence, the whole affair is forgotten.—E.

F

the quack puffed off his own nostrum as the only *specific for all disorders*, and the smirking and officious asseverations of the parasite, that " the Master was the greatest Man of the \* *Times*," excited much merriment. They distributed a hand-bill to the following effect :

" Porro unum est necessarium !" †

" DR. BRAGADOCIO BEHAUDER LIMBERHAM, from *Seville, Calcutta,* and *Balruddery*, renowned through three quarters of the globe, the kingdom of Ireland, and the town of Ramsgate, for his acquirements in all polite learning, and his endowments with all natural qualities.—He possesses all languages, he professes all arts, and flatters himself that he is a miracle of eloquence, genius, science, and several other particulars, which modesty and space forbid him to name. He is the sole inventor and proprietor of the wonderful pill which cures all disorders, and averts old age and infirmity; of which miraculous power the Doctor is himself a living example, having preserved to a great old age the perpetual spring of youth, as he is ready to exhibit to all ladies and gentlemen who may visit him. Hours of business from five in the evening till three-quarters before six.—N. B. *A back door to the Park.*"

\* Vetus's Letters appeared in the Times newspaper.

† The family motto of the Wellesleys. But it seems here quoted in allusion to the cry of Lord Wellesley's partizans, that his return to power was the *unum necessarium* to the national welfare.

Mr. *Ponsonby* was inimitable in Old *Dogberry:* the conceited emptiness of the old Constable, his affected pauses, ridiculous mistakes, and emphatical truisms, were copied to the life. The manner in which he assured his auditors that " *if he were as tedious as a King, he could find it in his heart to bestow all his tediousness on their Worships:*" and that " *he thanked God he was as honest as any man living, that was an old man, and no honester than he,*" was truly comic.

Lord *Lauderdale,* as the Devil with his tail chopped off, was prodigiously entertaining, though his Lordship supported the character without the assistance of a mask.

Mr. *Lambton,* as *Fauconbridge,* railed at the Duke of Austria in a very spirited style; and vindicated his preference of his own birth and blood over those of *Sir Robert,** with characteristic vivacity.

* An allusion to an attack (see p. 44.) on Lord Castlereagh, K. G. *Sir Robert* Stewart is his Lordship's legal style.

Mr. *Charles Wynne,* as *Speaker of the House of Commons,* Sir *Watkin* as the *Serjeant at Arms,* and Lord *Ossulston* as the *Mace,* were an admirable group. His Lordship, particularly, was exquisitely gilt, and supported the difficult character of the Mace with great perseverance and humour. Mr. *Greenhill,* as Mr. *Speaker's Secretary,* was as great a quiz as could be desired.

The Duke of *Norfolk* as *Silenus,* and Mr. *Hurst* * as his *Ass,* were very great.

Mr. *Brougham,* in the character of *Schedoni,* wore a real Neapolitan costume, which he had the honour to receive as a present from her Royal Highness the Princess of Wales, and looked very truculent and well ;—he passed most of the evening in close conversation with the *Neapolitan Minister.* †

Mr. *B. Gordon* was an excellent copy of a *Chinese*

---

* Robert Hurst, Esq. M. P. for Horsham.

† At this period there was no Neapolitan Minister at this court. Murat was still on the throne.—E.

*Joss,* which he represented without either mask or stuffing, and was admitted to be the most natural resemblance in the room.

Sir *Charles Monck,* as a *fresh-water Lobster,** excited much merriment by walking on his hinder claws, adorned with the insignia of the Bath. The inflexible gravity of his deportment, contrasted with the ridiculous figure he cut, was irresistibly pleasant.

Mr. *Will. Martin,* as a *Somnambulist,* talking in his sleep—The Marquis of *Douglass* as a *French lacquey*—Lord *Darnley* as *Jack Straw*—Sir *Samuel Romilly* as *Doctor Cantwell*—Sir *Frederick Flood* as *Father Foigard*—and several other excellent characters, which we regret we have not room to notice, added to the festivity of the evening; and it was not till a late hour in the morning that the gay fantastic scene finally closed.

* This seems to refer to a foolish story of the worthy Baronet's having had a place for keeping lobsters alive in his ponds in the country. The Baronet made a motion on the subject of the order of the Bath, sess. 1815.

# CHANGE OF ADMINISTRATION.

*March* 11, 1816.

No small sensation was produced in the House of Commons last night, by an intimation thrown out in the course of debate, by Sir Gilbert Heathcote, Bart. that there was a third Party in Parliament, neither devoted to the Ministry nor to the Opposition, from which it was more than probable that the Prince Regent—acting (as Sir Gilbert pointedly observed) in the name and on the behalf of his Majesty—would select the responsible advisers of the Crown.

The *projet* of such an Administration was circulated in the House, and having had the good fortune to obtain a copy of it, we give it publicity, without pledging ourselves to the truth of the report, or the precise details of the arrangement.

First Lord of the Treasury, and Chancellor of the Exchequer—Sir GILBERT HEATHCOTE, Bart.

Lord Chancellor—Mr. PRESTON,* who is to be called up to the House of Peers by the titles of Baron Doe and Viscount Roe.

President of the Council—Earl STANHOPE.

*Privy* Seal—B. GORDON, esq. with the Grand Cross of the Bath.

First Lord of the Admiralty—Lord COCHRANE—if forthcoming. †

Three Secretaries of State—Lord OSSULSTON, Sir CHARLES MONCK, and Mr. PETER MOORE.

Master of the Rolls and Secretary at War—Mr. WILL. MARTIN.

* R. Preston, Esq. M. P. for Ashburton; an eminent convey-ancer. He, as subsequently appears, took a very lively interest in agricultural questions, which he seems to have discussed with a warmth very unusual on such subjects.—E.

† Every body recollects Lord Cochrane's escape from prison about this period.—E.

## IRELAND.

Lord Lieutenant of Ireland—Lord NUGENT.

Chief Secretary—Mr. PEG. WHARTON.

Chancellor of the Exchequer of Ireland, with a Seat in the Cabinet—Sir FREDERICK FLOOD.

One of our reasons for disbelieving this report is, that, as our readers must have observed, in the above list, some of the most distinguished Leaders of Opposition are included. It is, however, on the other hand, but candid to admit, that in the course of the morning, Stocks experienced a slight rise.

If there be any foundation for this rumour, we conclude that Mr. B. GORDON will *drop his motion* relative to the Order of the Bath.

# A TRUE NARRATIVE *

## OF THE PHRENSY OF HURLOTHRUMBO VETUS, ESQ. IN A LETTER FROM SIR ——, BART. TO THE EDITOR.

December 10, 1812.

SIR,

As the phrensy of Mr. HURLOTHRUMBO VETUS has, of late, taken a more desperate turn, and as I feel my character in some degree implicated in the notoriety which has accompanied his last paroxysm, I trust you will have the goodness to give insertion to the following Narrative :—On the 6th inst. while at dinner with one of my most distinguished nervous patients, I was called home to speak with a person who came to request my immediate attendance on a Gentleman who was dangerously ill: as the messenger was only a poor old woman, who implored me with

* This is an obvious imitation of Pope's Narrative of the Phrensy of John Dennis.

nothing but tears in her eyes, I should have declined going, but as she told me the Gentleman's name was VETUS, and as I knew he stood remarkably well with my dear and noble friend the Marquis WELLESLEY, I consented to attend, and I followed the old woman as soon as my chariot was got ready.

When I came to his lodging, near the King's Bench,* up three pairs of stairs (which I should not have thus particularly mentioned, but that this lunatic conceals his place of residence, on purpose to prevent the good offices of certain charitable persons, who are bent, it is said, on effecting his cure by wholesome discipline,) when, I say, I came into his room, I found this unfortunate Gentleman in bed, with an Editor of a Newspaper standing on one side of him, and a † tall lusty Gentleman in spectacles

---

* It was reported that a person whose circumstances were embarrassed, and who lived in the *rules* of the King's Bench, wrote Vetus's Letters.—E.

† Probably Mr. Sydenham. See p. 65.

sitting on the other, whom I afterwards learnt was in the Excise. On my entrance, the patient frowned upon me, and cried out with violence, "'Sdeath, 'tis a spy from LIVERPOOL! there's a plot to betray me!" " Sir," said I, " here is no plot, but for your own good; and I never have been in Liverpool in my life: the recovery of your senses requires my attendance, and I have been sent for on no other account." I then took a particular survey of his person, and the furniture and disposition of his apartments: his aspect was furious, and he rolled his eyes about with great velocity; his hair was grizzled and short, and his beard of the same colour but long; his eyebrows grey and thick, and, with perpetual frowning, they were almost grown into one. I omit to describe his personal attire; suffice it to say, it was such as one would expect from one who for many years had been, from low circumstances, confined to these poor apartments: by the fire-side, there were a two-penn'orth of coals in a *Times* newspaper; and on the table (which had but

three legs) and the floor, which was not very perfect, there were piled huge heaps of paper of the
same title, which the old Nurse said she was sure
was the cause of his malady, and begged of me to
remove them from his sight.  There was nothing
neat in the whole chamber except a half dozen
books magnificently bound and gilded, which, notwithstanding my intimacy at * Apsley-house, I never
before heard of, nor, I believe, were any where else
to be found; such as " *The Marquis Wellesley's Official Correspondence with Foreign Ministers in the
years* 1810 *and* 1811."  " *Plans for sending the
Tower Hamlet Militia and the Light Horse Volun-
teers to re-inforce the Spanish army in the Peninsula.*"
" *A Project for raising* 1,000,000*l. in hard cash.*"
" *An Account of the Travels and Adventures of Fer-
dinand Count Kolli,*" † and " *An Essay on Public*

* At this period the residence of the Marquis Wellesley.—E.

† It will be recollected that the Moniteur published a story
of a supposed emissary of Lord Wellesley's, called Baron or Count
Kolli: the plan, as stated in the Moniteur, was too silly to be
believed of a British Minister.—E.

*Spirit.*" The only works I had any knowledge of were the Letters of the unhappy Gentleman himself, in two very thick volumes, and an old Play, called " *The Plain Dealer*," which I picked up from the floor, where it had been sadly soiled and trampled upon. On the table before-mentioned were also a few candle-ends, but no cheese-parings, that I observed ; a gallipot of ink with a yellow pen in it; and a pot of half-dead ale, covered with a LIVY, Latin and English.

As I was casting my eyes around on all this odd furniture with some earnestness and astonishment, I was somewhat surprised to hear the man address me in a very sober manner, to the following effect :
" Beware, Doctor, that it fare not with you as with your predecessor, the famous HIPPOCRATES, whom the mistaken citizens of Athens sent for, in this very manner, to cure the Philosopher DEMOCRITUS; he returned full of admiration at the wisdom of that person whom he supposed a lunatic." He continued in this strain for a considerable time, and

with much prolixity: but the chief marks of in-
sanity that I observed were, that he talked very
much at random; sometimes about Spain, and
India, and again about Russia, and TIPPOO SAIB,
but always in a very rambling incoherent manner,
and he proposed sundry wild and visionary schemes
for war, hostilities, and finance, so that it appeared
that the poor creature fancied himself a great General and Minister of State. In the course of his
speech, I felt his pulse, which was quick and irregular, and I perceived he had considerable swellings
in both legs. From this latter circumstance I concluded that the case might not be desperate, and I
began therefore to make some necessary inquiries;
but to avoid misrepresentation, I shall here insert
*verbatim et literatim* the whole conversation that
took place; for I make it a practice to keep an
exact memorandum of every word I interchange
with my patients since it has become the fashion to
print and publish the most private conversations; a
precaution recommended to me by my friend Mr.

SHERIDAN, * when I last met him and Mr. WHIT-
BREAD, Mr. CANNING, General MATHEW, Doctor DUIGENAN, Lord GRENVILLE, and the Duke
of MONTROSE, at dinner at my friend Mr.
DENT'S. †

DOCTOR.—Pray, Sir, how did you contract this
swelling?

VETUS.—By my lucubrations.

DOCTOR.—Lucubrations! Since I have been a
Doctor, and what is more, while I was an Apothecary, I never heard of such a distemper.

VETUS.—'Sdeath, Sir, a distemper? It's no distemper, but a noble exertion of my faculties; I
have sat fourteen hours at it, and don't you know,
that there's a communication between the legs and
the brain?

* About this time the minute details of some ministerial negotiations were published in all the papers, and Mr. Sheridan said,
in parliament, he would not venture to ask an acquaintance how
he did without taking a note of it.—E.

† It would seem that Mr. Dent's dinners are not always well
*assortis.*

DOCTOR.—But what has particularly disturbed you of late ?

VETUS.—Bathurst. *

DOCTOR.—Sir, I mean your distemper; what gave you this tumor ?

VETUS.—Bathurst, Bathurst, Bathurst !

OLD WOMAN.—For God's sake, Sir, don't name that evil spirit; my poor master was just getting quiet, when this devil of a *thrust* and a *thirst* threw him into these violent fits again.

THE EDITOR.—Fits ! zounds, woman, a man may well have swellings in his legs who sits writing fourteen hours a day. He got this by the *letters.*

DOCTOR.—The letters, what letters ?

VETUS.—'Sdeath, Sir, have you never read my letters ? not in the Times, nor yet in the Pamphlet ; I will be damned if this dog of an Editor has ever advertised or puffed them.

THE EDITOR.—There it is ! there's gratitude ! I

---

* Earl Bathurst's replies in the House of Lords to Lord Wellesley were peculiarly effective.—E.

published advertisement on advertisement; puff upon puff: if the pamphlet is not read 'tis no fault of mine, but of him who made it. By G— there has been as much done for it as for any pamphlet since Erskine's.

DOCTOR.—Let us not talk of letters and pamphlets, Sir; I fear those are the fuel that feed his delirium; you do very ill to promote this discourse. —I desire a word in private with this other Gentleman, who seems a grave sensible man. I suppose, Sir, you are his apothecary.

GENTLEMAN.—Sir, I am his friend.

DOCTOR.—I doubt it not: What regimen—— ?

OLD WOMAN.—Oh, Doctor, don't talk of regimens; that always sets him off in a fit : he talks for ever of sending a thousand of them off to Portingale and such outlandish places.

DOCTOR.—Silence, woman! Allow me, Sir, to continue my question; what regimen have you observed since he has been under your care ? You remember, I presume, the passage in Celsus, which says, if the patient on the third day have an interval, suspend the medicaments at night; let fumigation be used to corroborate the brain : I hope you have on no account promoted sternutation by Hellebore.

GENTLEMAN.—Sir, you are mistaken; I——

DOCTOR.—Mistaken; am I not a Physician *now*, and will an Apothecary dispute my opinions! You, and such as you, may have filled up a prescription or two of Baillie's which chanced to succeed, and with that very same prescription, injudiciously applied, you kill multitudes. *Pharmacopola componat, Medicus solus præscribat*, says Celsus. I understand both the profession and the trade, as well as any Baronet of 'em all. Mistake! I mistake! Fumigate him, I say, this very evening.

VETUS.—Hold, Sir! What, Sir, my friend an Apothecary! A base compounder of drugs? He who like myself professes the noblest science in the universe, Politics! Do you imagine that I would submit my writings to the judgment of an Apothecary?—By the Immortals he has had a hand in every letter of Vetus; he has written the finest tirades, and pointed the strongest facts; he has pounded the *Post*, curried the *Courier*, licked Liverpool, and bothered Bathurst.

THE EDITOR.—Doctor, you are in a small mistake here; this Gentleman is Mr. ——, an author —an occasional author. He wrote " Reasons for quitting the Cabinet." — " The Account of the Mahratta War," and several other admirable works which have been attributed to noble pens. He has got a place in the Excise by his writings, which is more than all your Addisons, Johnsons, and Steeles ever got.

VETUS (in a paroxysm)—Answer my question, caitiff Lord, or else you die. 1 shall make these *mountains* echo with thy obloquy.

DOCTOR.—Mountains! what is he at now?

OLD WOMAN.—Alack, Sir, my poor master fancies himself in the mountains : he calls this garret, a cottage ; the lead spout, a purling rill ; and the cats that squall in the gutters, bleating lambs ; and what's worst of all, poor Gentleman, he calls me Filly, and Cloe, and such heathenish names.

VETUS (the paroxysm continuing) — Wickedness totters on its narrow base—Magnanimity towers. The great Behauder walks abroad in full majesty ; his feet are on the earth, his head in the clouds. Burgos is not taken. Ciudad Rodrigo is surrounded. Salamanca is erased from the historic page : the army is disgraced : nations are overthrown : the world is no more ; and I am sick, very sick!

DOCTOR.—That's a good symptom ; a very good symptom. To be sick to death, say the modern Physicians, is an excellent symptom ; when a patient is sensible of his pain, he's half cured : pray, Sir, of what are you sick ?

VETUS.—Of every thing, of every thing ; abroad

and at home; in Spain, and in Russia; of Lord Wellington, Lord Cathcart, and Kutusoff; I'm sick of Burgos, and of Salamanca, and of Dorogobugsh. The great Drama—

OLD WOMAN.—The dram, Sir; the gin is all gone; but I'll fetch more presently.

VETUS.—O shameful want! scandalous omission! No reinforcements to the army, no reforms for the people, no places for his Lordship; no change, zounds, no change at all!

OLD WOMAN.—Pray, Sir, be not angry, and I'll fetch change.

DOCTOR.—Peace, good Woman; his fit increases. Pray, Mr. Editor, hold him.

THE EDITOR.—Plague on't; I'm damnably afraid they are in the right of it, and he is mad in earnest. If he should be really mad, who the devil will buy the " Letters?"—(*Here the Editor scratched his head.*)

DOCTOR.—Sir, I shall order you a cold bath

to-morrow: Mr. Editor, you are a sensible man; send for Doctor Simmons's people forthwith. The symptoms of his madness seem to grow desperate— (*at this moment I thought it right to get as near the door as possible.*)—We must eradicate these indigested ideas out of the pericranium, and reduce the patient to a competent knowledge of himself and others.

VETUS.—Caitiffs, stand off! unhand me, miscreants! Is the man, whose whole endeavours are to bring the country to reason, mad? Is the man, who would make war on conceptions of sublimity, mad? Is the man, who deposes Lords, and calls Marquesses to the helm of State, mad? No, the town is mad; the Parliament's mad; the nation's mad; all Europe's mad; but the reign of the incapables is at a close— the sun of impracticability rises. " Lord Liverpool, I have done—The British army starves ;—is unpaid, —and defeated. The people starve, are disappointed, —and disgraced. The mind of your Sovereign has undergone a revolution. England is roused, and you are ruined." *

At the conclusion of this speech the poor man's rage grew quite ungovernable; he started violently, and showed strong symptoms of hydrophobia. In order to ascertain the truth of my surmise, I came behind him, and emptied the jug of water on his head; at which he showed such violent rage, and so convinced me of the nature of his malady, that I made the best of my way out of the room, and had a narrow escape of a fracture, from falling against the old woman and the Editor, who had tumbled over one another down the stairs before me. I had, however, no other hurt but a slight contusion on the os coccygis, and I did not stop to inquire after the nurse and Editor, who, I trust, had broken one an-

* This and some other passages are extracted from Vetus's Letters, but much of the pleasantry is borrowed from the article on Dennis in Pope's and Swift's Miscellanies.—E.

other's falls, but proceeded to make a report of the case at Apsley-house.

This is, Sir, a full and true account of this transaction, and will, I hope, be satisfactory to the public, and put down all the idle tales at present in circulation. I am, Sir, your obedient Servant,

———— Bart.

## EPIGRAM.

Courier, Dec. 15, 1812.

" SIR ARTHUR's * military fame,

" I think," quoth VETUS, " with submission,

" Your Lordship honestly may claim,

" Because—you bought his first Commission !"

* Vetus had claimed for Lord Wellesley the merit of having advanced his brother in the army.

So when an eloquent Divine
    Was loudly praised for preaching well,
" Hold! not so fast, the merit's mine,"
    Quoth Sexton Tom—" I rang the bell!"

———————

# STATE PAPER.

The manner in which the most confidential papers have of late been betrayed to the public, will lessen the surprise of our readers at our having so early obtained a copy of the following letter from a *Gentilhomme Anglais* now in London, to his friend the Duke of Bassano at Paris: though it purports to be a private letter, our readers will perceive that it is in fact a most important State Paper, and well worthy public attention.

" TO HIS EXCELLENCY, MONSEIGNEUR, THE DUKE
OF BASSANO, &c. &c. AT PARIS.

" London, April 28, 1815.

" MY DEAR DUKE.—At last, after a most vexa-
tious delay, the plan of the *Constitution* has reached
England, and I hasten to give you, for his Majesty's
information, some account of the sensation it has
produced here.

" I grieve to be obliged to say, that it has not so
completely succeeded as we had promised ourselves,
and I fear the absurd prejudices of this besotted
nation as to the bad faith of the EMPEROR are not
likely to give way even to this document, though no
pains have been spared to prepare their minds for
the proposed change of character which he assumes:
indeed I regret to state to you, that he is almost as
unpopular in London as at Paris, and I doubt
whether your *badauds* can have regarded *the Con-*

*stitution* with more profound contempt than our Cockneys.

" The chief cause of ridicule against our Con-stitution is, that it is a mere experimental machine, which the EMPEROR never intends to put in force, and which, if he were sincere, could not act for want of practised workmen (if I may use the expression) to put it into motion—' you have Houses of Lords and Commons—Liberty of the Press— responsible Ministers—rights of petitioning,' say they, ' all upon *paper ;* but you have not the materials to make Lords, Commons, political writers, or independent petitioners.' This objection, we know, has no real force, because it is far from his MAJESTY's intention that the Constitution should ever be called into effect, unless indeed it be, like the machine of MARLY, once or twice a-year, to amuse the Parisians on a holiday; but, as, in appearance, it has some weight, and as I know his MAJESTY attaches so much importance to any colour of approbation which can be obtained from this country, I have thought of a scheme which may remedy the inconvenience, and which I trust you will submit to his MAJESTY'S consideration.

" As the machine itself is purely English, I propose that English artificers (to continue my metaphor) should be engaged to set it in motion; in other words, I propose to his MAJESTY to place some English gentlemen in the conduct of his affairs, and in the places made by the new Constitution. This may be done with perfect propriety on both sides, if, as I hope, we should succeed in maintaining peace between our countries.

" I dare not promise as to the persons I might be able to obtain for this purpose, as without his MAJESTY'S sanction, I have not dared to open myself at large to any person on so delicate a subject; but I have no hesitation in saying, that I think his MAJESTY would find that his opinions of certain individuals would not be deceived. Be that, however, as it may, I venture to suggest, whether, after the manner of the conductors of our Opera here, who hire at Paris second-rate dancers to be first in our ballets, I might not be authorised to endeavour to try to engage in London a company of *second-rate politicians* to set the Constitution a-going.

" Of course I should naturally turn my eyes to my own friends, or, as we call them, the *Opposition ;* firstly, because they never have exhibited that determined hostility to his Majesty which all other classes of the country have shewn ; secondly, because they are, in their and my opinion, the greatest statesmen and constitutionalists of the age ; and lastly, because I can have them, I believe, at a very reasonable rate.

" I do not promise myself that I should be able to engage any of the first-rate performers. Lord GREY, I apprehend, would hardly give up the place of first serious man at Westminster, to be a buffo at

Paris. Lord GRENVILLE, I fear, recollects his old quarrel with the Emperor, when First Consul. My friend WHITBREAD would do very well in many particulars, but as you have SANTERRE,* you would hardly want a person of that character; besides, I believe in my heart that we should not keep him quiet three days, and that he would be in Vincennes in the course of a week. Indeed, I consider personal vanity and selfish arrogance so much the great bases of his character, that if he were placed under the Emperor's Government, he would soon declaim against it, if he dared, as loudly as he does against his own.

" As to TIERNEY, I don't well know what to say. —With all the apparent phlegm of a John Bull, he is as versatile as a Frenchman ; and, indeed, I doubt whether he could be made any thing of, except in Opposition. His hostility might be advantageous to your budget, for we observe here that our financial

* Mr. Santerre was like Mr. Whitbread, an eminent Brewer.

affairs never succeed so well as under his denun-
ciations of ruin.

" Of Mr. PONSONBY, his own friends here would
give you a bargain; but I suppose he would hardly
be induced to move again at his time of life, as he is
considerably above 45 years old, which is the utmost
limit of age he allows to any political exertion, and
I really do not know what you could do with him,
unless it was to make him *Chancellor*—for which,
however, he would not answer much better than
our round little friend, CAMBACERES ; he has also a
pension in Ireland of 100,000 francs, which it might
distress your treasury to make good.

" I shall now proceed to mention to you some
other persons who appear to me to have the kind of
talent that would answer my design, if the continuance of a state of peace should encourage them
to make a tour to Paris.

" Sir GILBERT HEATHCOTE is an* old gentleman,

* I have not been able to discover why Sir G. H. is called *old*:
his appearance does not account for it.—E.

who, while I was in France, proposed himself, I understand, for the situation of Prime Minister in England *—his disappointment in that object might induce him to take a subordinate office; he might be elected one of the members for Gascony, and would be useful in laying down certain undeniable propositions very proper to be stated in the infancy of legislation.

" Mr. BENNET, if there is, as I said, a prospect of continued peace, would make an excellent Minister at War—*il a les manières gracieuses;* and utters, as poor TALLIEN used to do, the most vehement opinions and the most abusive language, in the mildest manner: he has, if I may use the expression, a polite emptiness of head and heart, which I think not at all ill suited (you will forgive my partiality for a friend) to the Parisian climate.

" Lord DARNLEY is a Kentish Nobleman, who has turned his attention chiefly to farming and sea

* (See page 70.)

affairs,* in which he is equally skilled. I wish I could persuade myself that he would accept the *Ministère de la Marine;* in the event of a war he might continue to hold that office, as there is no way in which he could better serve his native country.

" Mr. PRESTON, who was proposed as Lord Chancellor in Sir GILBERT HEATHCOTE's Administration,† is a perfect economist, and might be made equally useful as *Premier Procureur de S. M.*, or *President de la Société Agricole;* but he has the disadvantage of understanding neither farming nor French, on which account he has latterly employed himself in translating MIRABEAU's treatise on the Cultivation of Land.

" Lord KING, as *Ministre du tresor Public,* might have an opportunity of reviving a reputation on that subject, which lasted a few days amongst us

* It appears that the Earl of Darnley, about this period, made several motions on the subject of the naval administration.

† See page 70.

H

about ten years ago. He has not of late taken any great part in public affairs, as he has been ever since his first publication* closely employed in studying its meaning, and I hear he has still a great deal to do.

" Mr. HORNER, who is a lawyer and reviewer, might be very useful as Chief of the Commission for securing the Liberty of the Press. No man understands better the art of indulging himself in that liberty, which he represses in others. Indeed, the Edinburgh Review I have always considered as the work in this country most consonant to the EMPEROR's principles, and an admirable model for a Censorship of the Press.

" We have a certain Lord NUGENT here, whose figure would a little startle Madame la Duchesse; but he has notwithstanding a great head. He is the author of a beautiful poem, descriptive of Spain,

* Lord King had published several years before a pamphlet on exchanges and currency.

Buckinghamshire, and the Black Sea, which he called Portugal; and he has been now several years employed in bringing before Parliament the details of a rencontre between two packet-boats, in which one damaged the other's jib-boom. Both his Poem and the Parliamentary Inquiry prove how much he can write and say without making the least progress, and if there was any subject which you might wish to delay *sine die*, without venturing to abandon it altogether, you might find him very useful.

" Lord STANHOPE* might replace DE PREAMI-NEAU, as *Ministre des Cultes*. The Emperor himself has scarcely a greater aversion to Bishops than this Peer; indeed, I should say that there is nothing on earth he seems to dislike so much as the Clergy, unless it be the Lawyers. These, you will allow, are valuable antipathies to find in an Englishman. If he should fail as a Minister, he would still be useful at the *Vaudeville*, as he is a more entertaining

* The late Earl Stanhope.

H 2

caricature of our country than even JOLY. We English are not very merry, and, least of all English, we Peers of Parliament; but you cannot think how this admirable comic statesman contrives to keep us in a roar.

" As I suppose the Emperor would on no account part with the Duke of OTRANTO, MEIIE'E DE LA TOUCHE, or CARNOT, I know not to what use we could turn Sir FRANCIS BURDETT, Mr. BROUGHAM, or my friend Major CARTWRIGHT; in fact, any open connexion with them could not fail to do his Majesty the greatest injury in this country, and I really do not think they could be better employed than they are here.

" We have a Mr. LYTTELTON,* of whom probably you never can have heard, a county member, and though a silent politician, very facetious in society. This gentleman came into our Parliament with great expectations, which have been so utterly disap-

* The Hon. W. H. Lyttelton, M. P. for Worcestershire.

pointed, that I suppose he would be very ready to change a situation in which he is quite ' manqué.' As he is the most impudent man alive when he has no one to oppose him, and owes his success in table jests to this valuable quality, I imagine he might be very powerful in an assembly like yours, where the whole debate might be arranged beforehand, and Members should be forbidden to answer Mr. LYT-TELTON's pleasantries, on pain of *the Plain of Grenelle*.\*

" If the Department of the Leman had not been separated from France, Sir S. ROMILLY might, I apprehend, have been Member for Geneva, and would have replaced the Abbé SIEYES, when that worthy old man shall be called to his everlasting reward. I believe Sir SAMUEL to be well versed in the Code Napoleon, and very fertile in theories of law and legislation, suited to the meridian of France.

\* The scene of Buonaparte's military executions near Paris.

" I give your Excellency these general hints, and shall be glad to hear what you think of them. Adieu, my dear friend; I embrace the Duchess with all my heart—I never shall forget her goodness to me. Remember me to FLAHAUT and BIGNON. I fear the foreign negotiations of the latter will not last long : but FLAHAUT will gain what BIGNON loses. Tell NEY that I have searched all London, but in vain, for the picture of *Judas Iscariot*, which was advertised for sale in one of the public papers here, and which he so much wished to have. In fact, I believe it was a mere joke, aimed at TIERNEY, and that no such picture ever existed.

" Believe me to be, my dear Duke,

" With the most entire esteem,

" Your faithful friend and humble servant,

K.

" *P. S. April* 29.—I am sorry to say that WHIT-BREAD's absurd impetuosity has done a great deal of mischief; he brought on, in spite of all TIERNEY and I could do, the question of Peace or War last night, and after two rambling, rumbling speeches, had the question decided against the EMPEROR by a majority of *four* to *one*. Some of what are called here the most *respectable* of the Opposition, such as ELLIOT, GRATTAN, CALVERT, FRANKLAND LEWIS, &c. &c. voted against us. Our *respectable* men are all damn'd obstinate blockheads: we had, however, on the other hand, Sir HENRY MONTGOMERY, a new hand, and Mr. SWAN, an old one. I should mention to you that Mr. DOUGLAS, who visited the EMPEROR at Elba, has had the audacity to say, that the more he knew of the EMPEROR the less he was inclined to trust him. We thought we had him sure; but you see you must not reckon on any Englishman who has the least understanding. Mother Wit is always sure to go astray with us. Lord ALTHORPE, who spoke last night, is quite another sort of man, very thick and steady. Once more, adieu—and once more I embrace Madame."

# SEVERE BATTLE.*

April 20, 1815.

THE annals of pugilism have rarely recorded a more interesting combat than that which was fought near Westminster-bridge, on Monday, the 10th inst. between those noted candidates for pugilistic fame, Bob Stewart, otherwise *Bit of Blue*, and Sam the brewer. The challenge was sent by Sam, and as he had given notice of the fight some days before, the fancy mustered very strong.—Tom Wood † was second to Bob; bottle-holder, Brother Hiley. ‡ Will Martin *officiated* for Sam; bottle-holder, Joe Barham. §

The combatants fought in an oval ring, about 30

---

* See parliamentary debates of this date for a sharp discussion between Lord Castlereagh and Mr. Whitbread.—E.

† Tho. Wood, Esq. M. P. for Brecon, Lord Castlereagh's brother-in-law.

‡ The Right Honourable Hiley Addington, M. P. for Ipswich.

§ J. Barham, Esq. M. P. for Stockbridge.

feet by 10, which was surrounded by six or seven rows of seats, rising one above the other, and filled with amateurs of the first distinction. The battle lasted five hours and three quarters—but the combatants were in such excellent wind and training, that they never waited to take breath : and it can hardly be said that there were more than three or at the most four rounds. Odds at setting-to four and five to one in favour of the Irishman.

## THE BATTLE

Commenced at a quarter before five. The ring having been cleared by Serjeant Seymour. *

1st Round. No sparring—Sam set-to without much ceremony. He made three or four lounging hits at Bob's head; but it was evident that he misjudged his distance terribly. Sam acted in this round quite *on the offensive*, though he shifted his

---

* H. Seymour, Esq. Serjeant at Arms.

ground constantly, and threw a good many hits away to the right and left. Towards the end of the round, he lost his temper, tried a cross-buttock, but failed—and after an *irregular* struggle, was thrown on his back against the ropes.

2d Round. In this round the Irishman shewed himself a flash man, and as cool and determined a pugilist as was ever pitted: he sparred cautiously at first, parried all Sam's hits with much dexterity, and punished him about the head and body with the greatest good humour.—Sam seemed uneasy at this treatment : and at length Bob *took compassion on him*, and planted a left-handed facer on Sam's jaw, which floored him, and put an end to the round. —Lombard-street to a China-orange against Sam.

3d Round. Sam rallied, and sprang on his legs with much gaiety; his wind seemed untouched, and his jaw stronger than ever : he affected to make play, but the Irishman smiled with confidence. Sam tried to pink him below the waist: loud cries of "foul, foul," which Sam disregarded, and the battle went on, until the Irishman fibbed him severely, and Sam's friends took him out of the ring.

## OBSERVATIONS.

It was evident throughout the whole of the battle to the *cognoscenti* that Sam had no chance. He hit at random, and more than once pinked Brother Hiley the Bottle-holder, instead of aiming his blows right at the Irishman. Sam is a glutton, but has no more science than Ikey Pig. He has gained an easy victory over some provincial novices at the fairs at Bedford, and thinks he can contend with tip-top Professors. Immediately after the battle, Bob threw a summerset, and appeared as gay as ever. It is about sixteen years since Bob first appeared on the stage in his own country, and he was then thought a very promising plant.

## ENGLISH MELODIES.

### No. I.

It has been a subject of national reproach that the *English* have no national songs. Every body knows that the Irish and the Scotch have, by their National Melodies, just published, added to *their* reputation and to *our* humiliation, and even the Jews have of late found a *David* in Lord Byron, who has endeavoured to place them in the same scale (of the *gamut* at least) with their Christian neighbours.

A *patriotic* society of English individuals have determined, as far as in them lies, to retrieve our national character; and to enter the lists with the Irish, Scotch, and Hebrew Melodists.

A person of the name of Milbourne was said by Dryden to be the *fairest of critics*, because he published his own verses with those of his antagonists; and left the public to judge of the merit of the two productions. We, too, are ambitious of the praise of fair criticism, and shall in the same spirit exhibit to our readers the works, which our Society undertakes to imitate, previously to our laying before them our own performances on the same model. An impartial public will decide between the rival compositions; and our publication will be so far at least assured of success, that one half of it will be of acknowledged merit.

We shall begin (which may be called taking the *Bull* by the horns) with one of the celebrated *Irish* Melodies.

## SONG.

THE WORDS BY T. MOORE, ESQ.—THE MUSIC
ARRANGED BY SIR J. STEVENSON.

### I.

Oh! the days are gone when beauty bright

My heart's chain wove;

When my dream of life from morn till night

Was love—still love!

New hopes may bloom,

New days may come,

Of milder, calmer beam;

But there's nothing half so sweet in life

As Love's young dream!

Oh! there's nothing half so sweet in life

As Love's young dream.

## IMITATED.

THE WORDS BY JOHN CALCRAFT, ESQ.—THE MUSIC
BY C. W. W. WYNNE, ESQ.

### I.

Oh! the time is past, when *Quarter-day*
My cares would chase,
When all in life that made me gay
Was place—still place;
New hopes may bloom,
New offers come,
Of surer, higher pay—
But there's nothing half so sweet in life
As *Quarter-day!*
Oh! there's nothing half so sweet in life
As *Quarter-day.*

## II.

Tho' the bard to purer joys may soar,
        When wild youth's past;
Tho' he win the wise, who frown'd before,
        To smile at last—
        He'll never meet
        A joy so sweet,
        In all his noon of fame,
As when first he sung to woman's ear
        His soul-felt flame,
And at every close she blush'd to hear
        The one loved name.

## III.

Oh! that hallow'd form is ne'er forgot,
        Which first love trac'd;
Still, it lingering haunts the greenest spot
        On memory's waste!

## II.

Tho' I sit and vote with *Peter Moore,*
    Since all hope's past;
Tho' I win from those who *cough'd* before,
    A *cheer* at last;
        So sweet a cheer
        I ne'er shall hear
    From *Opposition* throats,
As when first I caught the Speaker's eye,
    And big with notes,
Moved the Committee of Supply,
    On *Ordnance votes !* *

## III.

Oh! never shall from memory fleet
    Dear Palace-yard! †
Still fancy haunts the envied seat
    Of *Robert Ward.* ‡

---

* Mr. Calcraft was Clerk of the Ordnance in the Talents' administration, and moved the Ordnance estimates.—E.

† The Ordnance Office in *Palace-yard.*

‡ R. Ward, Esq. M. P. for Haslemere, and now Clerk of the Ordnance.—E.

I

'Twas odour fled

As soon as shed;

'Twas morning's winged dream;

'Twas a light, that ne'er can shine again

On life's dull stream;

Oh! 'twas light that ne'er can shine again

On life's dull stream.

I triumph'd there

But *half-a-year,*

And touch'd but *half the pay !*

But oh !—I ne'er may touch it more

For half a-day ;

Alas ! I ne'er may touch it more

For half a-day !

# ENGLISH MELODIES.

## No. II.

WE to-day present our readers with one of Lord
BYRON's Hebrew Melodies, which for vigour of language, ease of versification, and magnificence of
idea, is one of the most admirable lyric compositions
in modern poetry.   Anxious, however, to fulfil our
engagement with the public, we have not feared to
enter the lists even with this excellent performance,
and we trust that our " *Debate on the Navy Estimates*"
will not be found unworthy our model.   We are not
authorised, much as we admire his work, to state
the imitator's *name ;* but, from the *ingenuous diffidence*
which such a silence implies, many of our read-

ers will suspect him to be the Honourable Mr. WILLIAM HENRY LYTTELTON, a gentleman who inherits at once the talents and modesty of his family.

" Ingenui vultus puer, ingenuique pudoris!"

## THE DESTRUCTION OF SENNACHERIB.

### I.

The Assyrian came down like the wolf on the fold,
And his cohorts were gleaming in purple and gold;
And the sheen of their spears was like stars on the
    sea,
When the blue wave rolls nightly on deep Galilee.

### II.

Like the leaves of the forest when Summer is green,
The host with their banners at sunset were seen;
Like the leaves of the forest when Autumn hath
    blown,
That host on the morrow lay wither'd and strown.

### III.

For the Angel of Death spread his wings on the blast,
And breathed in the face of the foe as he past;

## DEBATE ON THE NAVY ESTIMATES.

### I.

Old TIERNEY came down like a wolf on the fold,
And his phalanx of voters was boasting and bold;
And the noise of their cheering resembled the roar,
As you shoot London Bridge when the tide is half o'er.

### II.

Like the rose-bush of summer, all budding and green,
Their hopes, while the question was putting, were
seen;
But, in two hours contest, so blighted and shorn,
The bud was all gone; there remained but the
thorn.

### III.

For the breath of the Ocean came strong on the blast,
And bung'd up the eyes of old GEORGE as it pass'd:

And the eyes of the sleepers wax'd deadly and chill,
And their hearts but once heav'd, and for ever grew
　　　still!

### IV.

And there lay the steed with his nostril all wide,
But through it there roll'd not the breath of his pride;
And the foam of his gasping lay white on the turf,
And cold as the spray of the rock-beating surf.

### V.

And there lay the rider distorted and pale,
With the dew on his brow, and the rust on his mail;
And the tents were all silent, the banners alone,
The lances unlifted, the trumpet unblown.

### VI.

And the widows of Ashur are loud in their wail,
And the idols are broke in the Temple of Baal;
And the might of the Gentile, unsmote by the sword,
Hath melted like snow in the glance of the Lord!

And the hopes of his Party began to grow chill,

And their hearts quaked with sorrow, their voices
were still.

## IV.

And there lay black BROUGHAM with his nostrils all
wide,

But though they were curl'd, it was not with pride;

And the froth of Gray BENNET lay light on the turf,

And the mouth-piece of WYNNE foam'd with anger
and surf.

## V.

And there LAMBTON lay, more than commonly pale;

And there ugly BOB, with a face like a tail;

HARRY MARTIN awoke; even NEWPORT was dumb;

And BARING look'd almost as frightful as B——M.

## VI.

And the waiters at BROOKS's are loud in their wail,

And mute is the Holland-House Temple of Baal;

And the might of the party, in spite of big words,

Hath melted like snow, both in *Commons* and *Lords*.

## ENGLISH MELODIES.

### No. III.

WE this day offer to the Public an imitation, by Mr. DUDLEY NORTH,* of one of Mr. MOORE'S most celebrated Melodies.

Mr. NORTH (to whom even political prejudice cannot deny true wit and refined taste) felt that it would be presumptuous to attempt to rival the sweetness of expression and tenderness of thought which flow through this delightful song; he has therefore substituted for the vows of a lover the paternal remonstrance of a wise old politician to a giddy young one. It is however unlucky that, of *advice,* as of religion, it may be said, that those who happen to be most in want of it, are, of all men, the least capable of understanding it.

---

* Dudley North, Esq. M. P. for Richmond. Mr. North has the reputation of being a very agreeable companion, but his name seldom if ever appears in the debates of the House.

In one point we venture to believe that Mr. NORTH is at least equal to his model ; as the introduction of his talented * and venerable friend Mr. PONSONBY, instead of the Sun-flower, is surely " a glorious emendation," as Doctor JOHNSON says, " which places the copyist almost on a level with the original author."

* Talented, an Irish expression, equivalent to the English word clever.

## SONG.

### BY T. M. ESQ.

### I.

Believe me, if all those endearing young charms,
  Which I gaze on so fondly to-day,
Were to change by to-morrow, and fleet in my arms
  Like fairy-gifts, fading away !
Thou would'st still be ador'd, as this moment thou art,
  Let thy loveliness fade as it will,
And around the dear ruin each wish of my heart
  Would entwine itself verdantly still.

### II.

It is not, while beauty and youth are thine own,
  And thy cheeks unprofan'd by a tear,
That the fervour and faith of a soul can be known,
  To which time will but make thee more dear !
Oh ! the heart that has truly loved, never forgets,
  But as truly loves on to the close,
As the sun-flower turns on her god, when he sets,
  The same look which she turn'd when he rose.

## IMITATED.

### TO P. M—, M. P.

### I.

Believe me, when all those ridiculous airs,

Which you practise so pretty to-day,

Shall vanish by age, and thy well twisted hairs,

Like my own, be both scanty and grey,

Thou wilt still be a goose, as a goose thou hast been,

(Tho' a fop and a fribble no more)

And the world which has laugh'd at the fool of

*eighteen*

Will laugh at the fool of *three-score.*

### II.

'Tis not, while you wear a short coat of light brown,

Tight breeches and neckcloth so full,

That the *absolute blank* of a mind can be shown,

Which time will but render more dull;

Oh! the fool, who is truly so, never forgets,

But still fools it on to the close;

As PONSONBY leaves the debate, when he sets,

Just as dark as it was when he rose.

# ENGLISH MELODIES.

## No. IV.

THE Hebrew Melody, which is the present object of our imitation, is perhaps the least valuable of Lord Byron's, and our copy will not, we hope, be found at all inferior to the original. We are not at liberty to state by whom it is written, nor are we informed to whom it was addressed.

We are, indeed, inclined, from the internal evidence of the lines themselves, to suppose that they are addressed to a mere imaginary being, and that the poet has amused himself by collecting incongruities, merely to create perplexity; for how can a *rat* be the *son* of a *Lord?* it is a physical impossibility! and how can the son of a *Lord* be a *dealer in hats?* it is a moral absurdity!—How can a person who is, by law, " *Right Honourable*," be an " *apos-*

*tate?*" and how can another, whose peculiar distinction is " *Honourable,*" be a sorry *turn-coat?*

The lines are evidently no more than an ingenious riddle, the meaning of which (if it has any) we honestly confess we have not been able to discover.

## SUN OF THE SLEEPLESS.

### BY LORD BYRON.

Sun of the sleepless! melancholy star!
Whose tearful beam glows tremulously far,
That show'st the darkness thou can'st not dispel,
How like art thou to joy remembered well!
So gleams the past, the light of other days,
Which shines, but warms not, with its powerless rays;
A night-beam sorrow watcheth to behold,
Distinct, but distant; clear—but, oh how cold!

## IMITATED.

### TO THE HONOURABLE ————.

Son of the faithless! melancholy rat!
Whose circling sleeve still polishes thy hat,
Offering at once *thyself* and *it* to sell;
How like art thou to him remembered well,
The apostate Lord, the rat of other days,
Enrich'd, but never warm'd by Royal rays!
The rising Sun still watching to behold;
Clever, but callous; shrewd—but tame and cold.

K

# ENGLISH MELODIES.

### No. V.

" THE Leader's Lament," which we lay before our readers, in this number, is a happy imitation of the lines, which have within this day or two appeared, entitled " Fare thee well," and attributed to the pen of Lord BYRON; and we think we may venture to say, that though our imitation does not crawl servilely on all fours, it possesses almost as much tenderness and pathos as the original :* —

### THE LEADER'S LAMENT.

#### BY THE RIGHT HON. GEORGE PONSONBY.

Fare ye well—and if for Easter—
 Still for Easter fare ye well—
Till the call ye now released are,
 'Gainst the Serjeant none rebel.

* I have not thought it necessary to reprint this original, for several reasons.—E.

On those seats no longer snore ye,
  Seats so often fill'd by you,
While that placid sleep came o'er ye,
  Which my speeches lull'd ye to.

Would, before the Session's over,
  That the House could hear me through,
Then at last they might discover
  'Tis not well to *snouch* \* me so.

If *ye* do not choose to cheer me,
  *Ye*, who my adherents are,
Why, in silence can't ye hear me?
  Why cry " Question !" at the bar?

Though I may grow rather prozy,
  Though my jokes fall flat and dead,
Why must you, the first, get dozy?
  Why, the first, go home to bed?

---

\* Mr. Ponsonby on some occasion had used the word *snouch,* with what meaning is not clear.—E.

Yet—oh yet—yourselves deceive not—
    Though it be a bore to stay,
Thus to treat your Chief, believe not,
    Can to office pave the way.

Still those Ministerial faces
    Grin at *us*——still *ours* look blue—
And —— our curse!—they keep their places
    Still, whate'er we say or do.

Then when " Ay" they loudly hollow,
    Will ye stoutly echo " No!"—
And are all prepared to follow
    When I to the lobby go ?—

If my rival BROUGHAM should press ye,
    Listen not to him, I pray—
Will ye sorely thus distress me,
    Poor old Snouch thus turn away ?

Should his speeches e'er resemble
    Those which you have heard from me—
Well the Government might tremble
    Two such Orators to see.

All my jokes—you know but too well—
    All my dulness—none can know—
But our common hopes to do well,
    Wither—if you treat me so.

All our confidence is shaken,
    One may come, but many go;
By METHUEN join'd—by LEECH forsaken—
    E'en BANKES begins to smoke us now.

But 'tis done—debates are idle—
    Speeches from me are vainer still;
And Members whom no places bridle
    Must play the truant, when they will.

Then fare ye well !—thus disunited

　Like you, was never party seen—

Nor coughed—and quizzed—and sneered—and

　slighted,

　Like me has any leader been.

=========

## ENGLISH MELODIES.

### No. VI.

THE following *original* Song has been sent to us
from Nottingham :—It seems to be in praise of the
worthy Member * for that Town. We wish the Correspondent who has been so good as to transmit it
had intimated the Air to which it is to be sung; it
could not fail to become popular.

----

　* John Smith, Esq. seems about this time to have taken more
part than usual in the proceedings of the House of Commons.—E.

## I.

While every tongue,
Both old and young,
From Penzance to Penrith,
Is hymning PAUL,
Will no one call
Their thoughts to *Handsome* SMITH.

## II.

Taste, wit, and sense—
Without pretence—
Though PAUL be furnish'd with;
They scarcely are
Above the par
Of those of *Handsome* SMITH.

## III.

Wise Nature chalks
Them different walks;

Through Piccadilly's width
   Though PAUL may stride,
   Yet gay Cheapside
Exults in *Handsome* SMITH.

### IV.

Tho' FLOOD's the pride
   Of *Slaney's* tide,
And FINLAY of the *Nith ;*
   Old Father Thames
   A triumph claims
O'er both, in *Handsome* SMITH.

### V.

With blooming grace
   He decks his face,
And smiles to shew his teeth ;
   And old three-score
   Ne'er saw before
A Beau like *Handsome* SMITH.

## VI.

Surpassing, sure,

Both MONCK and MOORE,

In eloquence and pith;

The charms combin'd,

Of form and mind,

Unite in *Handsome* SMITH.

## VII.

Then Britain—round

From Plymouth Sound,

Even up to Pentland Frith,

Her voice should raise,

And sing the praise

Of *Wise* and *Handsome* SMITH.

# ENGLISH MELODIES.

## No. VII.

WE doubted whether we ought to publish the following Song under the title of an *English* Melody; but the author, the elegant and erudite Member for Glasgow, the *Roscoe* indeed we may say, of Greenock, assures us, that it is as good English as he ever spoke in his life.

After this testimony, we cannot hesitate to lay before our readers the following *English* Melody.

## THE BLACK BROOM.

A SCOTTISH SANG ; ENGLISH'D,

BY K. F.* ESQ. M. P.

To the tune of " *The De'il came fiddling thro' the town.*"

### I.

The Broom † cam capouring doon to the Hoose,

Wi' a *mossion* about an Excisemon ;

It sims the Exchequer can loosen a noose

Whech the law too cruelly teis, mon ;

So Looshington cried, " ye've foond a mare's

nest,

" We weesh ye much joy o' the prize, mon ;

" Tes a vera new grievance, but ane o' the best,

" Whan the Trasury snubs the Excisemon."

* Kirkman Finlay, Esq. M. P. for Glasgow.

† See Mr. Brougham's motion, on the 2d April, 1816, relative
to the remission of excise penalties.

## II.

The Broom is commonly pawkie enoo ;

  Boot was, faith, ilka night, not a wise mon,

Ef he thought, in the coontry, to make a hubboo,

  Wi' a mossion aboot an Excisemon ;

    For the Trasury cried, ye've foond a mare's nest,

      We weesh ye much luck o' the prize, mon ;

      'Tes a vara new grievance, boot ane o' the best,

      Whan the Trasury snubs the Excisemon.

## III.

The Exciseman is keen, *like a Wheg*, at a fau't ;

  *Like a Wheg* too, he staps at no lies, mon,

And so, 'gainst the honest plain dealer in mau't,

  Black Broom would support the Excisemon ;

    Then the Hoose all cried oot, ye've foond a

      mare's nest,

      We weesh ye much luck o' the prize, mon;

      'Tes a vara new grievance, but ane o' the best,

      Whan the Trasury snubs the Excisemon.

## IV.

There are *vots* on the Airmy, and *vots* on the Naivy,

For Aistimats aw' to revise, mon ;

Boot, aye, the best *mossion,* (and fair it, God saive ye)

Was the Broom's, just aboot the Excisemon :

For the coontry craid oot, ye've foond a mare's

nest,

We weesh ye much luck o' the prize, mon ;

'Tis a vera new grievance, but ane o' the best,

Whan the Trasury snubs the Excisemon.

N.

# GEOGRAPHICAL INTELLIGENCE.

## THE FRIENDLESS ISLANDS.

*April* 11, 1816.

A VESSEL just arrived *round about* from *New Holland* has brought an account of this interesting cluster of Islands, which had hitherto been little noticed by former circumnavigators. By some they have been mistaken for the Ladrones, but these are now ascertained to be exactly the antipodes of England, and to *lie* precisely opposite to the Cape of *Good Hope*. The following are the most remarkable of the group :—

*Twaddle Poon-son-boo,* the principal of the cluster, is very flat and uninteresting, but it is one of the richest of the whole, having an annual revenue of

4000*l.* of *our* money, which it derives from its dexterity in catching a species of *Great Seal.* *

*Teer-nee,* or Juggler's Island.—The character of this varies so much according to the side on which it is seen, that those who have viewed it only on one side would hardly know it again when they approach it on the other. The people are a shrewd, cunning race, famous for their expertness in legerdemain. They are, however, much distrusted by their neighbours, and it is a proverb in these islands, when they wish to express strongly the hopelessness of a search, to say, " You might as well look for truth in *Teer-nee,"* just as we talk of looking for a needle in Hyde-Park.

*Taf-fee-Wyn-nee.*—This is a most dismal island, being much infested with screech-owls, and the discordant noise perpetually produced in it by these

* Mr. Ponsonby having held the Great Seal of Ireland during the Talents' administration, had a pension of 4000*l.* per annum for life.

birds, combined with the hoarse croaking of a number of ravens, who also infest it, remind one of
fabulous stories of the stymphalides and harpies.
Mariners are recommended, when coming near it,
to adopt (though for a contrary reason) the precaution of Ulysses, and to stuff their ears with cotton
while they remain in its neighbourhood.  There is
such a surf breaks on its harbour mouth, that one
can seldom approach it without being covered with
spray.

*Pawlo ;* or, Booby's Island.—The inhabitants of
this are a singular race.  They are very low in the
scale of intellectual beings, but yet have all the
vanity of an intelligent people.  They are so little
to be depended upon, that they will *address* you one
day as a friend, and attack you the next as an enemy.
Strangers are advised to have as little to do with
these people as possible; and from their extreme
dulness, the scantiness of their resources, and cap-
tious temper, there is little inducement to hold any

intercourse with them—and indeed their sole support is derived from *petty war :*—their hair is short and curly—their features without the least expression—their countenances very grave and unmeaning, and they dress themselves very gaudily with a profusion of parrots' feathers. This contrast of solemnity and foppery is very ridiculous.

The island of *Francisco*, called by the natives, *Boor-dee-too.*—This island is nothing but a mountain, and is very barren and unproductive. It derived its first name from a *Jacobine Monk*, who was the first Missionary in those parts : he came round Cape *Horn*, and as long as a communication on that side remained, the island was pretty well supplied ; since that has been cut off, the people have been obliged to betake themselves to hunting ; but, from want of early habit, are but awkward in that pursuit. They are an extremely disorderly and turbulent race, though mild in their manners and appearance. An

L

old and strange account of this island is to be found in the Harleian Miscellany.

*Yan-kee*, supposed by some to be *Behring's** island, is evidently peopled by a separate race, who have, as the name imports, the strongest affinity to the Americans. These are the ugliest *race* of the whole, and the sounds they utter, as language, are hardly articulate.

*Hoo-too-shoo-poo-coc-a-too-hub-bub-boo*, or the island of *Coarse Broom*, which, it seems, is the meaning of this long and strange name. A most singular instance of *mirage* was observed on first approaching this island; its great promontory, or, in the sailors' language, its ness or nose, appeared to vibrate from one side to the other in a manner which the Captain of the vessel could only compare to the waving of an elephant's snout. This island is extremely mountainous in its interior: it is subject to the most violent tornadoes; but it is remarkable, that frequent

* A. Baring, Esq. M. P. for Taunton, a great American merchant.

as these storms of wind and thunder are, they are never accompanied by a single flash of lightning. The people are the most rough and rude of any of these tribes, and are indeed little better than intelligent *baboons*, whom they much resemble in face and shape: they are exceedingly mischievous; and they are little liked by the other islanders. With many of their neighbours they are in a state of perpetual war, and they have an old and deadly feud with the new *Hollanders*. They do not venture indeed openly to attack such formidable opponents, but lose no opportunity of making an incursion upon the *Hollanders* when they think they can do so unperceived and with impunity.

*Bum-mee* may easily be distinguished by its spherical, lumpish form, and the absence of any prominent features. The natives are supposed to be descended from some Hottentot emigration, as the distinguishing mark of that race is plainly to be recognised in the countenance of these islanders: they also resemble the Hottentots in this, that they seldom make their appearance in public without smearing themselves all over with *butter.*

*Jon-nee,* * called by the Portuguese *Porto Novo,* or Wasp's Islet, is full of the irritable and mischievous insects from which it derives its name. This little island is very arid and unproductive, and the people are a diminutive and dwindled race, very mischievous and passionate, as all dwarfs are.

*Ben-nee-too* is the Botany-Bay of the Friendless Islands : the shores are covered with a light foam, which is the only subsistence of the natives. Naturalists have not yet determined what this curious substance (if substance it can be called) is : in look it resembles the froth of small beer. †

---

* This would seem to mean John Warre, Esq. M. P. for Lestwithiel, an *Oporto* merchant.

† See note, p. 45.

*Kur-wee-nee*,* or the Hermit's Island. The inhabitants call themselves *Christian;* but if good morals are requisite for that designation, they are said to have but little pretensions to the name. They are a tall, swarthy, ill-favoured race; tolerably skilful in agriculture, and particularly in growing rape-seed.

*Craf-cal-lee.*—The inhabitants of this island have a general resemblance to those of *Paulo;* † they are indeed somewhat more intelligent, and their disposition to change arises not from imbecility of intellect, as with the latter, but from a very careful calculation of their own interests : they are great observers of the weather, and shift their places according to the appearances of the sky. Those of *Paulo*, on the

* This seems to allude to J. Christian Curwen, Esq. M. P. for Carlisle.

† Mr. Calcraft for a session or two took his usual seat in the neighbourhood of the Treasury bench, near Mr. Methuen; he subsequently returned to his old seat. Mr. Methuen, after he went into opposition, continued for some time to sit on the Govern_ment side.—E.

contrary, fickle as they are in other respects, never change their *old seats*. It is related that these two islands were formerly very close to one another; but that *Craf-cal-lee*, which is a kind of Australasiatic Delos, has lately shifted to a position, whence, as tradition goes, it had before moved.

There is a remarkable island, to which the natives have given the name of *Rat-tee*, * or *New-comer*, but which our sailors, in compliment to the Purser, called *Douglas's Island*. It is said to have but recently made its appearance in this group, and is supposed to be a volcanic creation : this hypothesis is confirmed by the general striated appearance of the surface, and by the continuance, even at present, of a constant eruption. It has hitherto been entirely unsettled; several parties have tried it, but none have quite ventured to trust themselves to it, for

---

* In parliamentary cant, members who change their party are called *Rats*, as that animal is supposed sagaciously to abandon a falling house. '

fear it should suddenly disappear from under them, like the island which appeared some years ago in the neighbourhood of the Azores.   It produces no vegetable but scurvy-grass.

There are various others of smaller note, making in all the number of about forty or fifty.

The Government of these Islands is a Federal Republic, of which *Twaddlo Pon-son-boo* is the nominal head; but in point of fact, they all set up pretty much for themselves, and they seem to have no great relish for any regular government at all: like all savages, the people are credulous in proportion to their ignorance; they have many pretended prophets among them, to whose predictions they listen with the utmost avidity, and they never seem to place less implicit confidence in the last new prophecy, because they have seen all former ones falsified by events :—Religion, properly speaking, they have none; and as to their morals and manners, the less that is said about them the better.   They have, however, some singular notions of a former and future state.  They believe that their race formerly occupied some pleasant seats on the other side of a large table or mountain, which is in sight of their present abodes : that they were driven out of them for some misdeeds by the *Great Breath* at the secret instigation of their evil genius Mumbo-Jumbo, * whom they represent as an elderly figure, with flowing white curls and dark bushy eyebrows, clothed all in black, and seated upon a fiery red throne, in shape somewhat resembling a great woolpack ; and they fondly cherish a hope, encouraged by the predictions of their prophets, that some day or other, when they shall have undergone sufficient penance in their present habitations, they are to be restored to those happy seats.  But the most intelligent among them secretly ridicule this expectation ; and are well aware,

---

* The change of the Talents' administration was chiefly attri-buted to Lord Eldon, now Lord Chancellor.—E.

that however such a notion may keep alive the hope and promise of *amendments*, little real improvement is to be expected from tribes, which rate so very low in the scale of intellect and manners.

---

## IMPORTANT STATE PAPER.*

THE following *Treaty* has not been laid before Parliament in *extenso;* though its results have been communicated to the House of Commons. Our readers will, we have no doubt, be curious to see the whole of this important and original document.

* This paper was intended to ridicule the alliance between Mr. Paul Methuen and the more violent part of the Opposition. The preceding articles leave us at no loss to determine that the Plenipotentiaries are Mr. Robert Gordon and Mr. Warre.—E.

## TREATY.

In the name of Wonder! Amen!

His Majesty Paul the 1st, Emperor of the Dandies, Autocrat of Himself and Grand Duke of Pantomime; and Henry Bruffham, President of the Republic of Billingsgate, and Protector of the Confederation of Palace Yard, being mutually desirous of entering into an amicable arrangement of all differences now existing between them, their States, subjects, and citizens respectively, have appointed as Envoys Extraordinary and Ministers Plenipotentiary, to treat of and conclude a Treaty of Peace and Amity, viz.

His Majesty the Emperor Paul, the most illustrious and honourable, the Sieur Jack-war, Count of Negus, Baron Blackstrap, Grand Cross of the Order of Temper, Knight of the Leaden Crown, Lieutenant in 2d Company of Lestwithiel Volunteer Infantry, &c. &c.

And the President, Robert, Baron de Bhum,

Grand-Gordon of the Legion of Despair, Knight of the Woeful Countenance, and of the Order of Cherabim and Seraphim, a Privy Councillor, and Member of the Council of State for the examination of Dutch Butter;

Who having mutually exchanged their full Powers, found in good and due form, have agreed upon the following articles :—

### ARTICLE 1.

There shall be from the date hereof an *offensive alliance* between the High Contracting Parties.

### ARTICLE 2.

His Majesty the Emperor Paul agrees to cede and abandon the province of Santa Fé, or Good Faith; but the President being desirous of giving the whole world a manifest proof of his moderation and generosity, declines occupying any portion of the said ceded province ; and it is hereupon concluded and agreed, that the said province of Santa Fé or Good Faith shall, on no pretence whatever, be kept by either of the High Contracting Parties, but shall form a separate State or Commonwealth independent of both.

## ARTICLE 3.

The President engages to furnish his Majesty the Emperor, for the ensuing campaign, a quota or contingent of as many *notions, motions, ideas,* and *propositions,* as his said Majesty may be able to *lodge* and *clothe.*

## ARTICLE 4.

His Majesty the Emperor engages to pay to the said President the full compliment of the said notions, motions, ideas, and propositions, whether he shall use and employ them or not, at a rate to be hereafter determined by Commissioners to be specially appointed for that purpose.

## ARTICLE 5.

His Majesty the Emperor further engages to restore to the said President, at the conclusion of the campaign, all the said notions, motions, ideas, and propositions, without any reserve whatsoever ; and furthermore, a reasonable compensation and allowance (to be determined as aforesaid) for the wear and tear, deterioration, and loss of value of the said notions, motions, ideas, and propositions, while in the service of his Majesty.

### ARTICLE 6.

If by the events of the war, or any other cause, the Lord Viscount Castlereagh should fall into the hands of the said *offensive alliance*, either as a prisoner of war or otherwise, it is hereby stipulated and agreed, that the sole charge and custody of the said Viscount shall be committed to the President ; well understood, however, that his Majesty the Emperor shall, by himself or his Special Commissioner in that behalf to be appointed, be permitted, from time to time, to look through the keyhole of the room in which the said prisoner shall be confined, in order to ascertain that he is safely watched, and interdicted from all external communication ; and in the event (which God forbid) of the escape of the said prisoner, his Majesty the Emperor engages to use all his * *address* to *catch* him again.

## ARTICLE 7.

Whereas the territories of his Majesty the Emperor abound in poppies, insomuch that opium is the staple commodity thereof, the President engages to take off as much of the said opium as he can bear, provided always that the said Emperor shall not attempt to export a greater quantity of the said opium than he has hitherto done, and that the President may continue to receive, at the rate of the tarif now subsisting, the opium, digitalis, and other narcotics of his ancient allies, neighbours, and confederates.

## ARTICLE 8.

And whereas the President is eminently desirous of diffusing and inculcating the most liberal and en-

* Mr. Methuen had, at Lord Castlereagh's request, seconded the address at the opening of the session.

lightened principles throughout the world, it is agreed that his Majesty the Emperor may attend as often as he pleases at Mr. Lancaster's school, founded by the said President, for the purpose of learning and attaining the arts, crafts, acquirements, or accomplishments of reading and writing; and his Majesty and the President do jointly and mutually engage to support and maintain, within their respective territories, a full, perfect, and uncontrolled freedom of speech and publication upon all subjects whatsoever; provided always that any disturber of the public peace who shall maliciously or contumeliously write or speak any words or matters, reflecting upon either of the High Contracting Parties themselves, shall be forthwith arrested and brought to execution without benefit of clergy.

### ARTICLE 9.

The present Treaty shall be ratified, and the notifications exchanged in the course of three weeks, or sooner if possible.

In witness whereof the respective Plenipotentiaries
have signed it, and have affixed thereunto the seals
of their arms.

Done at Westminster this 5th of February, 1816.

Signed         Signed

NEGUS. (L.S.)     DE BHUM. (L.S.)

---

## INFANTINE LYRICS.

SIR,—When you said that there were no *original*
English Melodies, you must have forgotten all that
amiable class of composition which amused you in
your infancy, such as "The Baby Bunting," "Goosey
Goosey Gander," " A was an Archer," and several
other ditties, very delectable to the ear of child-
hood, and which I presume to think are exclusively
national. I therefore presume that you will not be

displeased at my attempting to introduce some of those INFANTINE LYRICS to the public notice.

Men, it has been said, are no more than full-grown children; and I think that this apophthegm was never more truly applied than to that distinguished portion of our countrymen, to whom I dedicate my labours, and who in the common language are called *the Opposition :* as a sample of my work, I beg leave to submit to you my version of that celebrated deca-meter-monologue, which begins

" A was an Archer and shot at a frog."

I am, Sir, your obedient servant,

P. P.

---

### THE POLITICAL ALPHABET.

#### OR, THE YOUNG MEMBER'S A B C.

A, was an ALTHORPE, as dull as a hog;

B, was black BROUGHAM, a surly cur dog;

C, was a COCHRANE, all stripp'd of his lace;

D, was a DOUGLAS, who wanted a place;

M

E, was an Ebrington, dismal and dumb ;

F, was a Finlay, a hogshead of scum ;

G, was a Gordon's *preposterous* phiz ;

H, was a Heron, a damnable quiz ;

J, was Joe Jekyl, whose law is a jest ;

K, was a Knox, in a *sinecure-nest ;*

L, was a Lambton, sour, saucy, and sad ;

M, was Paul Methuen !—a Dandy gone mad ;

N, was big Nugent, who " Portugal" writ !!!

O, was an Ossulston, small as his wit ;

P, was poor Preston, stark mad about oats ;

Q, was a Quin, who with neither side votes ;

R, was dark Romilly's hypocrite look ;

S, was a Sefton,—Lord, coachman, and cook ;

T, was Tom Thompson, a tinker from *Hool ;*

V, was a Vernon, an * *asphaltic* fool ;

W, was a Warre, 'twixt a wasp and a worm ;—

But X, Y, and Zed, are not found in this form,

* One of Mr. V——'s speeches was laughed at for a mataphor about the fruits of the Asphaltic lake.

Unless MOORE, MARTIN, and CREEVY be said,
( As the *last* of mankind) to be X, Y, and Zed.*

=====

## INFANTINE LYRICS.

SIR,—Your kind reception of the first number of
my *Infantine Lyrics* emboldens me to offer you some
other specimens. In the ancient song of *Goosey
Gander*, short as it is, there are two points of serious
instruction. The first is, that *geese* ought not to
wander into situations for which they are naturally
disqualified; the second is, that old gentlemen, who
happen not to recollect what they have been *taught
to say*, are treated with contempt and kicked down

* The editor has supplied the names to the initials, which only
appeared at first. He believes he has made no mistake, as the
allusions are very plain from other articles of this collection.—E.

M 2

stairs. These fine moral sentiments, which are couched, in the original, in allegorical or rather hierographical obscurity, I have endeavoured to bring more home to men's business and bosoms; and if, by the example of one old Lord, I can deter another from making a goose of himself, I shall consider that I have been useful in my generation; and I shall not repent the great care, pains, trouble, and solicitude which I have bestowed in translating (if I may use the expression) this interesting allegory, which, though it be pretty generally known, I, as a proof of my fidelity, do not scruple to lay before your readers.

P. P.

Goosey, Goosey Gander,
Whither do you wander?
Up the stairs,
Down the stairs,
In my Lady's chamber.

Old Father Long-legs would not say his prayers;
　　Take him by the left leg,
　　Take him by the left leg,
　　Take him by the left leg,
And throw him down the stairs.

———————

TO THE RIGHT HONOURABLE LORD G. C. * ON HIS

GIVING NOTICE OF A MOTION.


　　Goosey, Goosey Gander,
　　Whither will you wander?
　　　Example take—
　　　(Or down you'll break)—
　　From the other chamber :

* Lord George Cavendish.

Poor Johnny Bedford could not say his speech ; *
    But he moved his right leg,
    Then he moved his left leg,
    Then he cried, " I pardon beg"—
And sat upon his breech !!!

O.

=====

# MEETING AT BURLINGTON HOUSE.†

A VERY full meeting of the Opposition took place
yesterday morning at Lord George Cavendish's, at
Burlington House, to consider the course of pro-

* It seems from the parliamentary debates, that the Duke of
Bedford had about this time stopped suddenly before he had
finished his speech.—E.

† Such a meeting did take place.—E.

ceeding to be adopted by the Noble Lord on his motion this evening. The Noble owner of this splendid mansion opened the business to the party in a short, and, as far as we could catch his meaning, satisfactory manner. He apologized for the liberty he had taken in requesting their attendance at his own house, but his respectable friend, Mr. Ponsonby, having made over to him the *lead* of the Party upon this occasion, he thought it most in form to do so. The task he had undertaken was one of some difficulty, and if he could collect *the sense* of the meeting, he was sure it would be of the greatest use to him. His intention, as far as he had considered the subject, was to move for the appointment of a *Parliamentary Commission, with full powers to make such reductions in every part of our military establishments as they might think proper;* and if he succeeded in carrying this motion, of which, however, a fuller attendance on this occasion would have given more sanguine hopes, he should move that it consist of Mr. Tierney, Mr. Bennet, Lord Folkestone, and Sir Francis Burdett. (*Murmurs.*) In proposing the three latter names, his Lordship stated that he was influenced by considerations of great importance to the interests of the whole Whig Party: he was sorry to say that another meeting on the same subject was now holding at Mr. Brougham's lodgings; and it was to conciliate that meeting, and to bring about, if possible, a union of all real Whigs, that he wished to propose three persons who he understood were at this moment at Mr. Brougham's; but he thought the present company would feel that by placing Mr. Tierney at the head of the Commission, there was a sufficient guarantee for the fairness, candour, plain-dealing, and attention to *general interests* only, which ought to characterise such an inquiry. He begged further to explain, that his motion would include the Ordnance; and that if it were to be successful, he would, on a future occasion, propose to establish a similar commission for dismantling the navy, which would consist of Mr. Tierney, (who had already given ample proofs how thoroughly he understood the subject), and Lord Cochrane. His Lordship concluded by begging to have the opinion of the meeting as to the various points of reduction on which it might be proper more particularly to insist.

Mr. TIERNEY expressed himself very sensible of the delicacy of the compliment paid him, and assured the Meeting, that having studied the Navy Estimates during the whole of the recess, he felt himself now a match for any body on that question : with regard to the Ordnance, however, though an undoubted economist, he hoped the Corps of *Sappers* and *Miners* would not be included in the reduction.

Mr. CALCRAFT would not have been the first to propose any *exceptions* to the general reduction which the Noble Lord had in view ; but as his Right Hon. Friend had set the example, he must take leave to say, that he trusted the Commission would have a liberal consideration for that head of service called the * *Unprovided.* He begged also to state, that as Maidstone was so short a distance from *Rochester,* he thought it absolutely necessary to keep up the *depôt* at the former place.

Lord ALTHORPE, with reference to his notice about the Leather Tax, did not see why in time of peace we might not revert to the ancient and constitutional practice of making our artillery of leather, instead of following the Continental fashion of having them of iron or brass. He was sure it would be very acceptable to his constituents, and would be a great relief to the grazing part of the agricultural interest, for whom, as yet, nothing had been done; and it was obvious how much better such a material would be for the *galloping* guns and the *light* artillery; at the same time that it would be by no means dangerous to liberty.

The Honourable Captain WALDEGRAVE appeared

---

* Mr. Calcraft was supposed not to be unwilling to take office —he was member for Rochester.

inclined to oppose this proposition, when he was tartly answered by Mr. WARRE, who had just joined the Party, that he had two very strong testimonies in favour of this leathern artillery; one theoretical, and the other practical : the first was from *Dyche's Universal Spelling Book*, a work of great authority (which he had lately been surprised to find that his Hon. Friend near him, Mr. Methuen, had never read). In this author it is directly stated, that, for the purpose of sieges and fortifications, *" there is nothing like leather."* The practical authority to whom he alluded was a gallant veteran whose reputation was well known to Gentlemen, but whose name, to the disgrace of the Government, he could not find on the pension list—he meant *Captain Shandy*, who, as might be found in that profound historical work called the *Elegant Extracts*, had made use of leather artillery on all his campaigns.

On the general subject, he begged to say, that his mind revolted at the reduction of the cavalry ;

but if it must be at all reduced, *humanity* to the *horses* required that they should neither be sold nor shot, but should be allowed for the rest of their lives to feed in places, now wholly useless, but which might be very well spared for the purpose; he meant St. James's and the Green Park, and the centre of Grosvenor, Golden, Hanover, Soho, Berkeley, and Russel squares, and Lincoln's-inn-fields.

The meeting shewed some little impatience at the length of Mr. Warre's observations ; upon which

Mr. METHUEN said, that he felt himself called upon by the flattering allusion made to himself to say, that he entirely agreed in all that his Honourable Friend had said, and he must also add one word in favour of the *Deserter* Corps, which he hoped would not be given up.   They might indeed be stigmatised as *Condemned* Regiments, but the use of things was not to be judged of by their names only.   He believed desertion to be a very general *offence,* and he knew instances of men who had deserted within a fortnight from the party with which they had enlisted.

Mr. FREDERICK DOUGLAS concurred in the observations made in favour of the *Deserter Corps,* and was encouraged by what had dropped from others to recommend the Corps of *Voltigeurs* to the favour of the Meeting. The rest of the army, he thought, might safely be *extirpated.* *

Lord SEFTON, though but lately admitted to such deliberations, hoped he should be forgiven if he strongly protested against any reduction in the *Driver Corps;* he also set great value upon a *good Commissariat* Establishment.

Mr. PONSONBY had not given any opinion hitherto, that he might not appear to dictate to the Meeting; but the short view he had taken was to reduce all that part of our Establishments which might be termed *active,* but to be indulgent to the *superannuated list.*

* Mr. Douglas in the House of Commons had talked of extirpating the French army.—E.

Mr. GORDON differed with Lord Althorpe about the Artillery; he was for getting rid of the *Field Trains,* to which his Noble Friend seemed partial, and for maintaining no Ordnance whatever but *Bombs.*

Mr. CURWEN hoped the Commissioners would reduce the number of Chaplains; but he would not have them touch the *Flotilla on the Lakes.* He begged, however, to observe on the danger that there was from the numerous Ordnance depôts scattered through the country: he himself knew an instance in which *a spark* had caused an explosion, which had excited the greatest alarm in a part of the country; indeed, one young woman was said to have been lost on the occasion, and several respectable families were thrown into a state of the greatest distress. *

Lord STANLEY was only sorry that the motion

* Here and in other places there are allusions to a story of a strange piece of gallantry, which, whether true or false, had certainly made Mr. C. very unpopular.

went no further ;  he would give the Commissioners
a general control over every branch of expenditure ;
and particularly the *Civil List*, which they had all
of them done their utmost upon all occasions *to
diminish*.  He could not bear to see public money
lavished in providing the Sovereign with the *splendid
magnificence* of *Thatched Cottages*.  If the Sovereign
wanted a temporary residence in the country, were
there not abundance of excellent houses all along
every great road, which, by the ostentatious display
of the Royal Escutcheon, seemed as it were peculiarly set apart for such purposes ?—*(Hear, hear,
hear !)*

Lord FOLKESTONE, who had just come in from
Mr. Brougham's, concurred in thinking the motion
much too limited; the Commissioners should have
far ampler powers, and should be authorized to act
in some degree as Censors, to check the military
spirit which pervades all ranks from the highest to
the lowest.  Why, he would ask, since we were
now at peace, did the Royal Liveries continue

*scarlet?* He thought it a dangerous symptom; it was an innovation, he believed, first introduced by the Hanoverian family, and a practice wholly unknown in the good times of Harry VIII. and Elizabeth. Why, too, were our soldiers tricked out in the foppery of red uniforms in time of peace, as if brown coats would not keep their backs just as warm and dry? He should never think the Constitution safe till he saw the Foot Guards exchange their gaudy equipments for the modest garb of Special Constables, and what was termed in the modern phrase, the Household Cavalry, assume the appearance of the Surrey Patrole.

Lord MILTON entirely agreed with every thing which had fallen from his Noble Friend, and could not help wishing that the attention of the Commissioners might be specially directed to those well-known Personages *Gog* and *Magog*. Their present warlike appearance must have a great tendency to keep up military ideas among the otherwise peaceably disposed citizens, and both as a matter of taste and of constitutional principle, he thought their martial costume should be exchanged for a Common Councilman's gown, and a full-bottomed wig.

Lord GEORGE CAVENDISH thanked his friends for their attendance, but observed, that as there seemed unfortunately to be a considerable difference of opinion among them, he trusted that in the Debate they would confine themselves to the most general topics, and not descend into particulars. A doubt having been started whether Mr. Bennet would be able to spare time from his prison inspections, to act as Commissioner, it was agreed that Mr. Creevey should be appointed in his stead. Some further conversation passed in a mysterious manner, which our Reporter, who was obligingly posted by Lord Duncannon behind one of the Elgin Metopes,* could not distinctly hear, and the Meeting soon after broke up.

* The Elgin marbles were still at Burlington House.—E.

N

# AN EXCELLENT NEW SONG.

To the old tune of *" A Cobbler there was, and he lived in his stall."*

YE noisy Reformers who rant and who bawl,
Come listen to me, while I sing you of Paul; *
Not him † who, at Putney, gave Burdett a fall,
But the worthy successor of Westminster Paul.

Ye Billingsgate muses, ye dames of the Hall,
Come sing from my ballad the praises of Paul;
We Poets of Grub-street, who write for the stall,
Had never a fitter Mæcenas than Paul.

* Evidently Paul Methuen, Esq.
† James Paul, Esq. (since deceased) wounded Sir F. Burdett
in a duel on Putney heath.—E.

If the air of a 'prentice, the face of a doll,
Were beauties, how lovely a creature were Paul;
If a wig-block well painted the heart could enthrall,
Even Freemantle's self could scarce rival our Paul.*

If a west-country tone, 'twixt a stutter and drawl,
Were eloquence, Lord, what a speaker were Paul;
If a noddle with no more of brains than a ball
Were a head-piece, Oh dear, what a Statesman were
    Paul!

You'd swear he was bred up at Coachmakers' Hall,
Such a *spouting* and *four-in-hand* Dandy is Paul; †
Had you seen him, when last he *enacted the Wall!*
Even *Moonshine* grew pale, and knocked under to
    Paul.

* These seem to allude to Mr. Freemantle, Secretary of the
Treasury in the Talents' administration, who certainly wears a
wig, but whether he deserves the imputation which the rest of
the line conveys is not so clear.—E.

† Mr. Methuen was famous in private theatricals; it is presumed
that he also belonged to the four-in-hand club.

He swears he belongs to no party at all,
And truly no party acknowledges Paul;
But, just as the Lion employs a Jackall,
The Whigs are so good as to tolerate Paul.

He had heard of the sudden conversion of Saul,
And thought changing sides was befitting a Paul;
But the Hebrew got reason and light by *his* fall,
But dulness and darkness still stick to *our* Paul.

His like we shall ne'er see again, all in all,
If any thing ever should happen to Paul ;—
And now should the sense of my Song appear small,
I beseech you remember, my subject is Paul.

# FAILURE OF THE BUCCANEERS, AND LOSS OF THE BROOM FIRE-SHIP.

———

March, 1816.

IT is with the liveliest satisfaction that we announce to the public the failure of the above enterprize, and the total destruction of the Broom fireship, in an action in St. Stephen's Bay, during the night of Wednesday, the 20th instant. This Buccaneer expedition was destined for a *coup de main* against the royal arsenals in Treasury Harbour, which they intended to plunder and burn, if they could not keep permanent possession of them.

Up to the above-mentioned day the fleet had proceeded with apparent success, under the command of the Ponsonby flag-ship, an old hulk fitted up for the occasion: it consisted principally of the Tierney hired trader, the Wynne, armed *en flute,* the Monck, a North country collier, the Milton, a heavy lugger, the * Curwen *tender*, the Broom fireship, the Gordon bum-boat, accompanied by some other Callcraft. †

On Monday the 18th, they had gained a considerable advantage over a squadron of revenue cutters, led by the Vansittart, which they defeated in Property Roads, by the assistance of a fleet of *country ships*, whom they decoyed to their aid by hoisting false colours. The Vansittart, however, we are happy to say, was not much damaged by the action, and though driven to the Straights for the moment, will soon be refitted in the London Docks. This partial success seems to have emboldened the Buccaneers, and in some degree to have hastened their defeat, by relaxing the discipline of the squadron. They began to disregard the signals of

---

* Another allusion to Mr. Curwen's importunate gallantry.—E.

† This is a mistake of our correspondent; it should obviously be *small*-craft. Mr. Callcraft had now rejoined the Opposition.

the Ponsonby, and many quarrels arose about the future distribution of their captured booty. On the evening of the 20th, as they were standing on under easy sail, the Methuen, an empty vessel, leading the way, the Broom fire-ship insisted upon running in to blow up Fort Regent: the Ponsonby flag-ship remonstrated against the attempt, alleging that they should only lose time by it; that the defences of Fort Regent were strong, and they were sure of being repulsed; that it would create an alarm, and raise the country people against them; and that it would be better to wait till they had got possession of Treasury Harbour, and then they might demolish Fort Regent at their leisure. The Broom, how-ever, relying upon her store of combustibles, and particularly the quantity of brimstone she had taken on board, disobeyed orders, and setting all sail, stood right in upon Fort Regent, blazing away on all sides. It was soon observed, however, that her fire was ill directed, and that more of her shot hit her friends than the Fort, and the rest of the fleet therefore hauled off, and stood aloof from her, contenting themselves with cheering her as she bore down in her attack.

The mistake made by the Broom now became manifest: a tremendous cannonade was opened upon her; she tried to *manœuvre* to get out again, but failed; she missed stays, and mismanaged her *royals*, and she was soon so dreadfully cut up that she lay like a log upon the water. At this time a fresh fire was opened upon her flank by the Martello tower on the Banks, supported by a detachment from the Saintes, and this completely silenced her.

The night was now so far advanced as to put an end to the engagement. The Broom was now seen *lying* in a pitiable condition. Her friends, however, determined to make an attempt to get her off, and about five in the afternoon, the Ponsonby sheer-hulk, and the Tierney hired trader, accompanied by the Bennet convict-ship, and the Gordon bum-boat, came down into St. Stephen's Bay, in order to try to tow her out. The Broom, however, would not answer the helm, was found quite unmanage-able, and although she seemed to float for a moment, yet a well-directed fire, which was in-stantly poured into her from Castle-Ray, laid her upon her beam ends again.

What is now to become of her we have no means of guessing; whether they will attempt to get her under way with a *jury* rigging, or appropriate her to the *press*, we know not. It seems certain that all the captains of the other ships would object to her ever being again brought forward in the line of battle.

# THE TRIAL OF HENRY BROUGHAM
# FOR MUTINY.

---

## SITTINGS BEFORE LORD GRENVILLE AND A SPECIAL
## JURY OF THE WHIG CLUB.

HENRY BROUGHAM was indicted, in the usual form, on the three following counts :

1st. That the said Henry Brougham hath, on sundry occasions, treated with disrespect the rightful and legitimate Leader of the Party, viz. the Right Honourable George Ponsonby, contrary to good manners, and the said George, his place and dignity.

2dly, That he, the said Henry Brougham, hath, at sundry times, made divers propositions or motions, without having communicated the same to the

Right Honourable George Ponsonby,—such conduct being contrary to the Rules and Regulations of
the Party—disrespectful to the Right Honourable
George Ponsonby, and unbecoming the character of
a Member of Opposition.

3dly, That he, the said Henry Brougham, did, on
or about the 29th March, declare to a Member of
Parliament, that it was his opinion that the Right
Honourable George Ponsonby was " an old woman,"
or words to that effect.

The charges being distinctly read by Sir W. W.
Wynne, the Prisoner pleaded not guilty.

Counsel for the Prosecution, Sir Arthur Pigott;
Mr. Charles Wynne.

For the Prisoner, Mr. Abercrombie; Mr. Bennet;
Mr. Lambton.

Sir A. P. opened the case in a short speech of
about two hours and a half, in which he took occasion, as explanatory of the present charge, to read
the Annual Mutiny Bill verbatim, and to insist on

the absolute necessity of good order and discipline in all constituted society; he then proceeded to call witnesses on behalf of the Prosecution.

The Right Honourable George Ponsonby.

Q. You are a Member of Parliament? A. I am.

Q. I believe, Mr. Ponsonby, you hold the office of Leader of the Opposition? A. I do.

Q. Is it an office of honour and distinction? A. It is *not*, to the best of my knowledge.

Q. I beg your pardon, I had been misinformed. Do you know the Prisoner at the Bar ? A. I do.

Q. Has he interfered with your rightful Privileges as Leader of the Opposition ? A. I consider that he has interfered very unwarrantably. He has made motions and put questions without consulting me. In particular, he made a motion respecting the affairs of Spain, without giving me any intimation of it.

Q. He left you wholly ignorant and uninformed

on the Spanish question? **A.** Wholly ignorant and uninformed on that and every other subject.

**Q.** In consequence of the unwarrantable conduct of the Prisoner, have the functions, duties, and profits of your office been diminished? **A.** They have.

**Q.** On what matters do you now occupy yourself? **A.** I put questions to the Chancellor of the Exchequer as to the day on which he will bring forward any particular business—I move for the printing of papers presented to the House—I state my opinion, that I am not bound to commit myself until the papers are printed and in the hands of Members—I call order when Mr. Pascoe Grenfell is speaking, and so forth.

*Cross-examined by Mr. Abercrombie.*

**Q.** Pray, Sir, by whom were you appointed Leader of the Opposition? **A.** I do not feel myself bound to answer that question.

Court.—The witness is not bound—State secrets are not to be disclosed.

Q. Pray, Mr. Ponsonby, how long did you hold the office of Chancellor of Ireland? A. Seven months—and five days.

Q. Did you receive any, and what Pension, in retiring from that office? A. I now receive *four thousand pounds* per annum.

Mr. Abercrombie.—The witness may go down.

Mr. Lambton. — The witness has been *going down* for some time past. (*A loud laugh.*)

## Mr. Kirkman Finlay.
*Examined by Sir A. Pigott.*

[It being stated that the Witness had some difficulty in explaining himself in English, Mr. ———— was sworn interpreter.]

Q. What is your name? A. Finlay, of Glasgow.

Q. Your Christian name? A. Caarkman.

Court.—What is the witness's name?

Sir A. Pigott.—Kirkman, my Lord—in my brief.

Q. What is your profession, Mr. Finlay? A. A Member of Parliament.

Q. Do you know the Prisoner? A. I do.

Q. Where have you seen him? A. In debating sacieties i' the North.

Q. Do you recollect the 26th March? A. I do.

Q. Did you observe any thing particular in the conduct of the Prisoner towards the Right Hon. George Ponsonby on that day? A. I ded.

Q. Relate what you observed to the Court? A. The House was in Kommitee, Mr. Ponsonby had rose to spak, but the Prisoner having rose after him, parsiisted to spak, and tapped him on the shoulder, and said " Set down—set down, I'm in possassion of the Kommitee."

Q. Were you in a position from which you could see the action of the Prisoner? A. I was— I was setting behind the Trashery Bench.

*Cross-examined by Mr. Bennet.*

Q. As the witness sits behind the Treasury Bench, perhaps he also goes to the Treasury ? A. I do constantly.

Q. Do you frequently communicate with the Treasury? A. Constantly.

Q. Then I ask you, Sir, whether you do not support the Government? A. Upon my *oth* I do not.


Lord Duncannon.

*Examined by Sir A. Pigott.*

Sir A. Pigott.—Please, my Lord, to turn your head to the Court.

Q. What are you ? A. Son to the Earl of Besborough.

Q. I mean what is your profession or occupation ? A. I am whipper-in to the Opposition, and occasionally report for the *Morning Chronicle.*

Q. You know the House of Commons well? A. I do.

Q. Do you consider the Prisoner at the Bar to be of the least use to any Party? A. Yes—of the greatest use to the Party he opposes. (*A laugh.*)

Q. Have Members of the Opposition complained to you of the conduct of the Prisoner? A. Frequently.

Q. Have the goodness to name one? A. Peg Wharton.

Q. What was Mr. Wharton's observation on the Prisoner? A. He said he thought he was a cursed bore, or something to that effect, and that he could not understand him.

Q. Do you recollect any other? A. Yes—Mr. Plumer.

Q. Did Mr. Plumer make any comment or cri tique upon the Prisoner? A. He said " he was a d—d long-winded Lawyer," and repeated the same thing fifty times over.

Q. What do you mean? was it Mr. Plumer or the Prisoner who repeated the same thing fifty times over? A. Both.

o

Sir A. PIGOTT observed, that he should now proceed to establish the 3d charge against the Prisoner —namely, that he had called Mr. Ponsonby " an old woman." He observed, that this charge would rest on the evidence of an informer—admitted this was always suspicious evidence—but strongly urged that it was not to be always and altogether refused* He called the Hon. Frederic Douglas.

### The Hon. Frederic Douglas.

Q. You are an independent man, I believe, Mr. Douglas?    A. I am.

Q. You are in the habit of conversing indiscriminately with men of all political parties?    A. I am.

Q. And each man with whom you converse would suppose you to belong to the same party to which he himself belongs?    A. Of course—if he did not know me.

Q. Have you ever conversed with the Prisoner at the Bar?    A. I have.

Q. On what occasion? A. The Prisoner had made a speech, which I understood as an attack on a Great Person, and I told him I thought it was a fine speech.

Q. What answer did the Prisoner make? A. He said, It was—a very fine speech.

Q. Did you make any other observation? A. I said, I thought he (the Prisoner) ought to be Leader; and asked him, in confidence, what he thought of Mr. Ponsonby.

Q. What did he answer? A. He said Mr. Ponsonby was an old woman, and ought to be turned to the right about.

*Cross-examined by Mr. Abercrombie.*

Mr. Abercrombie.—Put down your hat, Sir, and answer my questions.

Q. You have had the good fortune, I believe, Mr. Douglas, to have belonged to every party in the State? A. I cannot quite say that—I have not been long in public life, but I have been tolerably indiscriminate in my connexions.

Q. You told the Prisoner that you wished to see him Leader ? A. I did.

Q. Now I ask you, upon your oath, whether you did not tell Mr. Vansittart that you thought him a mischievous firebrand ? A. I did, but that was last Session.

Q. Has any inducement been held out to you to inform against the Prisoner ? A. I do not understand the question.

Q. I ask you, upon your oath, whether you expect any advantage from informing against the Prisoner ? A. (after some pause) I do not.

Q. You have no promise or expectation of place or preferment held out to you by the Prosecutor or his friends ? A. I do not deny that I have an expectation or promise.

Q. Then I ask the witness how he dare affirm that he expects no advantage from the information he has given? A. I beg to state, that I see no inconsistency at all. I have a promise, but little or no expectation; every body knows that promises of this nature are not always fulfilled.

Q. What place were you promised? A. Clerk of the Kitchen.

Q. Was that the place you applied for? A. No, I wished to be Secretary of State.

Q. What answer was made to this wish? A. That there were already sixteen candidates for Secretaryships of State, (exclusive of Mr. B. Gordon, and Mr. P. Moore) and that I had no chance.

Case for the prosecution closed.

The Prisoner attempted to set up an alibi, by the waiter of the Exchequer Coffee-house, but failed, it being clearly proved that he had spoken thirty-two times, on the night on which he alleged he was absent from the House.

Several witnesses to character were called.

Messrs. Creevey, Cochrane and Cobbett, General

Ferguson, Mr. Grant, Mr. Wishart,* and Mr. Paul Methuen, severally spoke to the Prisoner's character.

The Prisoner being called upon for his defence said, he threw himself upon the mercy of the Court. He was willing to retract any thing he had ever said—solemnly denied that he had meant any thing disrespectful to Mr. Ponsonby by calling him an old woman, and saw nothing in the character of old women that should make it a matter of reproach to be likened to one of that respectable and valuable class of society.

The Jury, after a very long deliberation, found the Prisoner Guilty, but recommended him to mercy, on the ground of his having vilified the Prince Regent. But his Lordship, from the Bench, acquainted the Jury, that he should not transmit this recommendation. He would, however, postpone passing sentence till the end of the Sessions.

* This person is not in parliament: he is supposed to be one of Cobbett's and Cartwright's men.

## ON MR. METHUEN'S SUPPORT OF LORD ALTHORPE ON THE LEATHER TAX.

Methuen and Althorpe, silly fellows,
What are ye, but a *pair of bellows*?
Two *wooden flats* that act together,
Connected by a band of *leather*!

PUFF.

## THE WILTSHIRE LETTER.

A WORTHY Gentleman has received a letter from *Wiltshire*, which he shews about with an air of so much satisfaction, and with so many expressions of *triumph* over the COURIER, that we feel ourselves in candour obliged to give it all possible publicity, in order that this attack upon *us* may speak for itself.

The letter itself is short and pithy, as a letter of business ought to be. The sting is, like a wasp's, in the tail.

### A LETTER, &c. to P. M.—M. P.

Dear Sir, We, your faithful Constituents, hope,
That you'll strongly oppose the New Duties on Soap.
We are, &c. &c.
THE SOAP-BOILERS OF PIMPERNE,
For Selves and Fellows.

### POSTSCRIPT.

To you, in return, due thanks shall be paid ;
We'll believe not a word that the COURIER hath
said—
That your vanity's great — that your wit is but
small—
That your surname is PRIG—or your christian-name
PAUL.

# ELGIN MARBLES.

A proposition is to be this day made to the House of Commons by Mr. Bankes, for the purchase of the Collection of Athenian Sculptures, commonly called the *Elgin Marbles*. We have heard it said that no opposition would be made to this proposal; and some persons have even asserted that nothing *could* be said against it. We, however, feel that much may be said, and we lay before our readers the following abstracts of what we think may very probably and very properly be said against Mr. Bankes's proposition.

Mr. Hugh Hammersley, for instance, may with great propriety observe, "that this question is next in national importance to the *Austrian Loan*, and that he hopes to procure for it more attention than he has been able to obtain for the latter." He may object to the purchase at an enormous price of cer-

tain *blocks*, called Elgin Marbles; and he may express a hope that before he sits down he may be
able to convince the House that there are *blocks*
enough at home without sending to Athens for
them.—He will next, probably, reprobate the mode
in which Lord Elgin obtained these marbles.  It
has been asserted that they were in a process of
destruction; that the Turks fired at them as marks;
" but what," Mr. Hammersley may justly ask,
" what does that signify? the Turks had a *right* to
fire at them, and God forbid we should interfere
with the rights of any other people ! Suppose that,
in this country, the Board of Ordnance should choose
to fire at *St. Paul's ;* suppose, even, that they were
to place a couple of howitzers on Ludgate-hill, and
batter down the great cupola—I put an extreme
case; but would even *this* justify the Turkish Am-
bassador in carrying off the rest of that noble edifice
to his lodgings in Fludyer-street, and afterwards
shipping it in transports in the river, consigned to

the Waivode of Athens? If it would not, what right had Lord Elgin to convey the Parthenon (which I understand to be the St. Paul's of Athens) to this town? what is sauce for the goose is, as the poet expresses it, sauce for the gander."

Mr. Hammersley might next proceed to object to the *price*—" they were valued at 35,000*l*. Thirty-five thousand pounds!!! He had seen them, and a more worthless, dirty heap of rubbish he had never set eyes on; they were old, dusty, chipped and broken. He had taken some pains to ascertain the price of statues, and he might inform the house that Mr. Rubble, an eminent stone-mason in the New-road, would make a complete set of *new* statues for one-tenth of the sum proposed to be given for those which were only *second-hand*. Nay more, he might have the pleasure to state that a respectable artist on the other side of Westminster-bridge, Mr. Coade, had invented a composition which was fire-proof; and he had ascertained that Mr. Coade would be happy to make a *bran-new* Theseus for 25*l*. This native artist would also undertake a female figure with a head for 15*l*. and yet it is proposed to give ten times that sum for a female figure without a head; fit for nothing, if he might presume to be jocose, but the sign of the *good woman*, which he had seen over some shops in the city.

" As for Scaphaphoræ,* Metapes, Hygeias, and Quadrigas walking in procession, he knew nothing about them; but this he did know, that Mr. Coade would engage to make a complete *Britannia*, with a *Lion and Unicorn* to match, all as large as life, for a less sum than Lord Elgin charges for a *horse's head;* and a full length statue of the Thames, with an urn, two oars, and a swan, may be had cheaper than the river Ilissus, which has neither urns, nor oars, nor even a head; and what is a *river* without a *head?*"

Upon the whole, however, Mr. Hammersley, with

---

* The mis-spelling of these words was probably intentional, and they are therefore left as they originally appeared.—E.

his characteristic liberality, may probably propose some degree of remuneration to Lord Elgin; and he would, we think, be likely to conclude with the following resolutions:—

1. That the value of the Elgin Marbles, estimated according to Mr. Coade's proposal for making new ones, is 448*l*. 7*s*. 9½*d*.

2. That Lord Elgin has no right to the said sum of 448*l*. 7*s*. 9½*d*. nor to any other sum whatsoever on account of these marbles.

3. That a sum of 25,000*l*. be, therefore, presented to the Earl of Elgin, as a mark of the disapprobation of this House.

4. That the whole of the said Marbles shall be, with all convenient dispatch, sent back to Athens, consigned to the joint care of the Captain-Pacha and the Mufti, in order to the speedy re-establishment of the Cathedral of the Parthenon in that ancient city.

5. That, with a view of making amends for the

spoliation of the said Cathedral, and of marking the
liberality and taste of the British Nation, a sum not
exceeding 120*l.* be granted to his Majesty to make
good the defects of Theseus and the other Goddesses
and Statues in general, previous to their being returned to Athens, and that the City Members and
the Members serving for the home counties, all the
Members for Ireland, and Gentlemen of the Long
Robe, be a Committee for the Repairs of the said
Goddesses and Statues.—(Hear, Hear!)

There will be, we dare say, no want of Members
desirous to second these motions; but we can imagine
no one more likely to catch the Speaker's eye than
Mr. GORDON, who may observe " that these statues
are in such a state of mutilation, that several of them
are deficient in the most important and weightiest
particulars : the front side of the Ilissus, and the
backside of the Theseus, are greatly damaged : the
torso of Neptune is worse even than the torso of the
Belvidere : every body knows the latter is perfect

from the neck to the knees; but the former is broken off at the waist, and wants one of the most graceful, characteristic and prominent rotundities of the human form. He cannot sit down, on the whole, without deprecating this purchase, and he may hope that his ' round unvarnished tail,' for he did not affect eloquence, will have its due weight with the House."

Sir JOSEPH YORKE * will take a favourable opportunity of intimating, " that he'll be damned, if he consents to any such thing. If we are to give thirty-five thousand pounds for *stones*, let it be for stones that can be of some use; stones for a breakwater in the Needles, or a new dock and wharf-wall under Dungeness." The gallant Admiral will probably express his surprise at such a proposition coming from Mr. Bankes, whom he always looked upon before as *a steady* fellow; and as for the *Report* of the Committee, it will seem to him a damned farrago

* Rear-admiral Sir Joseph Yorke, one of the lords of the admiralty, M. P. for Sandwich.

of outlandish lingo, and he may assert that one half
the Members present, if they would but confess the
truth, can neither make head or tail of it; and for
his part he believes the *Report* is like the statues
themselves, which, by the account of the Honourable
Gentleman who spoke last, have neither *heads* nor
*tails*.

Mr. MACDONALD * may observe, that he understands from Mr. Payne Knight † that these marbles
are so corroded and pitted by the effects of the
weather and time, that Minerva looks as if she had
had the small-pox; and he may assert, on the same
learned authority, that the marbles taken collectively
are wholly worthless for the only purpose to which
Mr. Knight considers such things as applicable,
namely, for household furniture. Mr. Macdonald
may state his own opinion that *surface* and a *polish*

---

* James Macdonald, Esq. M. P. for Sutherland.

† Mr. Knight gave some evidence to this effect before the committee on the marbles.—E.

appear to him to be valuable, far above all other qualities, and he therefore cannot consent to purchase what have neither.

Mr. SHARPE * will probably dissent from the arguments of the last speaker : he cannot rate *mere surface* so highly, and thinks there may be considerable merit even when the exterior is greatly corroded, and that the insinuation relative to the small-pox might have been spared. He will express his thanks to the Committee for having set the country right on the important point of the quantity of the penultimate of the word Phygalya, which he, for one, did not know before ; and he will hope that in future the City of Alexandria will be called Alexandrya.

Mr. BROUGHAM will, perhaps, detain the House with " *only one single* observation"—he will take leave to enter—register—and record his formal and solemn dissent—disavowal—and protest—against this

---

* Richard Sharpe, Esq. M. P. for Portarlington.

most atrocious—most flagitious—and unusual proposition for the bargain—sale—and transfer—of the
*Panathenaiac* marbles; for it was a gross abuse of
terms to denominate or call them *Elgin,* and he will
tell the House, *why :*—" Because when his Majesty's
*lieges* are asking for *bread,* you propose to give them
*stones*—When the manufacturers of Birmingham
are out of work, you are playing at marbles—When
the gardeners of Isleworth were, no later than
January last, out of employ—when the fen-men of
Ely are in insurrection, the Honourable Member
proposes, forsooth, to throw away the sum of thirty-
five thousand pounds!—a sum which, at the rate
of a shilling a head, would afford a substantial meal
for twenty times thirty-five thousand honest, hard-
working manufacturers—he proposes, forsooth, to
spend this monstrous—this alarming sum of public
money in the purchase of a few wretched, mutilated
blocks, which, as my Honourable Friend tells us,—
and I am sure the House is obliged to him for the

information,—that Mr. Payne Knight has declared
to be—what?—valuable?—no; in good taste?—no;
of our own manufacture?—no; but mere dirty, corroded surfaces, little better than that pagan idol the
Apollo of Belvidere."

Mr. Brougham may probably speak for two hours,
and touch upon the thousand and one points connected immediately or remotely with the subject;
for such, we are well aware, are the eloquence and
ability of the Honourable Gentleman, that it is far
easier for him to speak a speech of any length than
it is for ordinary Members to listen to it.

Mr. PONSONBY will probably close the debate by
observing, " that he knows not what to think of the
matter, as he has not yet had an opportunity of
reading the papers; but thus much he will take
upon himself, even in the present state of his information, to assert, that if any public money is to
be voted for the purpose, this House, and this House
only, has the constitutional right of voting the said

money; but he will express his earnest hope that his Honourable Friend (to whom the country is so largely indebted for bringing forward this motion) will not push it to a division, as he himself and several of his Honourable Friends are entirely ignorant which way it might be proper to vote."

## EXTRAORDINARY PARLIAMENTARY DEBATE.*

THE following Paper has been communicated to us by an ingenious Gentleman who acts as one of our Reporters in the House of Commons.

MR. EDITOR.—As you expressed a wish to have a written account of the extraordinary dream which I lately related to you, I willingly comply with your desire.

* The idea of this article is taken from an Irish publication.

I had been reading, one morning last week, Mr. Carpue's ingenious essay on making noses and lips, by cutting flesh for that purpose, from other parts of the body; I had also happened to dip into Doctor Spurzheim's fanciful Theory of the Characteristic Organization of Skulls; and when, on my return from attending the debates of the House of Commons that night, I had retired to rest, these three subjects continued, it seems, to occupy my mind, and they mingled themselves (as our sleeping thoughts usually do) in such a strange and yet ingenious confusion as to produce in my mind the following extraordinary succession of images and ideas.

I thought that one evening, when I, as usual, took my place in the back row of the Gallery, the House appeared uncommonly crowded, and a general expectation seemed to be entertained as if something extraordinary was about to take place.

I soon observed, indeed, that the Clerks, Messrs.

Dyson, Lee, and Rickman,* were not in their usual chairs, which were occupied, to my great astonishment, by Sir Everard Home, Mr. Cline, and a tall elderly Gentleman, whose name I did not know. Instead of inkstands, pens, and paper, which usually covered the table, I observed several cases of surgeon's instruments; saws and knives of various sizes, lint, bottles of styptic, &c. Whilst I was looking on this strange preparation with equal surprise and curiosity, the elderly Gentleman before mentioned, who sat in Mr. Lee's chair, and whom I heard the Speaker call to by the name of Doctor Spurzheim, stood up and read a paper entitled " *The Report of the Craniological Committee.*" This Report was very detailed, but the substance appeared to be that with a view of procuring unanimity in this difficult crisis of the Country, and of effecting a solid union of parties and persons on

* Three clerks of the House of Commons.

both sides of the House, a mutual interchange should take place between the several leading men of a part of their skulls, by which, as the report stated, there would be effected a union of organs, and of course of feelings and opinions, which could not but conduce to harmony, by creating a coin. cidence of temper and judgment between persons, however opposite to each other they might have previously been.

When the report was read and agreed to, the Speaker addressed Mr. DAVIES GIDDY, who, methought, had been the Chairman of the Committee, and directed him, in an authoritative tone, to " *name his skulls.*" Upon which the Hon. Member handed up a long list of names.

Mr. CHARLES WYNNE then spoke to the *order* of the proceedings; he had read the Journals four times over, twice backwards, and twice forwards, but was not able to find any precedent exactly in point. Lord Russell and the late Mr. Algernon

Sidney's cases, *tricesimo quarto, Caroli secundi,* were the nearest; but as these two Members had lost the *whole* head—tam sinciput quam occiput, as Sir Simon D'Ewes expresses it,—he would not propose it as a precedent to be implicitly followed on the present occasion.

After some further discussion on the law of Parliament as to Members *losing their heads*—in which the case of Messrs. Lethbridge and Pochin, and the more recent case of Messrs. Brougham and W. H. Lyttelton,* were referred to—it was settled that the House should be called over in pairs, and that Hon. Members should be put into the hands of Sir Everard, and Mr. Cline respectively, each of whom, after sawing off the hinder part of his patient's skull, should hand it to his Colleague, to be placed on the other head.

* These four members were supposed metaphorically to have lost their heads on particular occasions; Mr. Brougham from over zeal, the other three by forgetting the speeches they had prepared.—E.

All preliminaries being thus arranged, Mr. Speaker standing up, exclaimed with a loud voice, " The House will be pleased to be silent while their skulls are sawing," and immediately called upon Lord CASTLEREAGH and Mr. TIERNEY.

The Noble Lord obeyed without hesitation, but the Right Hon. Gentleman seemed rather to hesitate, and muttered, methought, some reflections on Mr. Speaker's partiality in selecting him for one of the first subjects of so dangerous an operation. The House, however, took the Speaker's part very warmly, and Mr. TIERNEY was obliged to acquiesce. The Noble Lord and the Right Honourable Member now knelt down, and laid their heads on the knees of the respective Surgeons, who with the proper instruments, and with astonishing skill and celerity, cut off the crown of each head, and interchanging the sections, through the means of Doctor Spurzheim, who sat between them, placed with great dexterity Mr. TIERNEY's occiput on Lord CASTLE-

REAGH'S head, and his Lordship's on Mr. TIER-
NEY'S: upon which they both rose up and returned
to their places, bowing to the Chair.

Methought I now overheard Sir Everard Home
remark to Mr. Cline, that he had never dissected a
sounder head than his Lordship's, that all the parts
were disposed in the most perfect order, and that he
never discovered in animal conformation a stronger
promise of sound judgment and moral excellence.
Mr. Cline whispered, in reply, that *his* subject had a
very different appearance, for that all the organs,
nerves, and muscles, particularly of the brain, were
tangled and twisted into a thousand turnings and
doublings, like the trail of a woodcock.

The effect of the operation was immediately
visible; Mr. TIERNEY'S manner became open and
candid; he spoke, indeed, in a more involved and
intricate style than usual, and he frequently talked
of *hinges, features* and *bottoms,* but then his matter
was so good, his principles so noble, and his feelings

so upright and honourable, that it was easy to see that he made a strong impression on the whole House, and, strange to tell, even his own friends appeared to place the greatest confidence in him.

Lord CASTLEREAGH, on the contrary, began to speak in a plain, matter of fact, intelligible manner, but what he gained in style he appeared to lose in substance; for notwithstanding his affected plainness, it was evident that there was always some little paltry trick or dexterity at bottom: the House was indeed much amused at his sallies, but he made no sort of impression; the Members on his own side appeared to place little confidence in him, and even Mr. ROBINSON and Colonel WOOD seemed to regard him with evident marks of distrust.

Mr. Speaker next mentioned the names of Mr. CANNING and Mr. PONSONBY; but he at the same time submitted to the House whether it would be consistent with their usual courtesy to their own Members that so strong a measure as cutting off half his head should be taken in Mr. CANNING's absence. This observation produced a discussion, in which the Members on the *opposition* benches insisted that what the Speaker had urged as a difficulty was, on the contrary, a facility, as it was certainly much easier to have a *cut* at Mr. CANNING in his absence than in his presence. Methought however that the sudden arrival of Mr. CANNING in a travelling dress put an end to the debate on this point, and as the friends of Mr. PONSONBY expressed a very strong desire that he should get a share of Mr. CANNING's brains, the latter Right Hon. Gentleman, after a short explanation from Mr. HUSKISSON of the arrangement which had been made in his absence, accompanied Mr. PONSONBY to the table.

When the operation was over, Mr. PONSONBY's manner was quite altered; his eye shot fire, his countenance was illuminated, his gestures were at once lively and graceful, his conversation became in the highest degree entertaining; every thing he said was either new or put in so happy a point of view, as to have all the graces of novelty: his language was at once admirable for its precision and its spirit; and every thing he said was received with attention and applause.

Mr. CANNING in the meanwhile slunk away to his seat with his hat pulled down over his eyes. He said very little, and that little was attended to by no one on either side of the House. Indeed there was so much coughing and confusion while he spoke, that I could catch but a few words here and there, such as "*two and two make four;*" from which I collected that he was either repeating the multiplication table, or calculating the retiring pension of an ex-Chancellor. But what seemed to me most extraordinary was, to observe Lord Binning and Mr. Sturges Bourne quizzing Mr. Canning, and laughing immoderately at old Twaddle, as I overheard them calling him.

The next couple that presented themselves were
Mr. VANSITTART and Mr. GRATTAN: as soon as
the interchange of their heads was effected, the
most surprising alterations became visible in their
deportments; Mr. VANSITTART began to throw
himself into the oddest postures imaginable, and to
play all manner of antics; he strode up and down
the House, as if he was measuring ground for a
duel; when he spoke his action was so violent, that
I observed he scratched off the skin of his knuckles
against the *floor;* ever and anon he gave the red
box on the table a thump that electrified the House;
his style was wild and desultory; he dealt chiefly in
short enigmatical sentences—intentionally antithe-
tical—and unintentionally profane;—the country
Gentlemen seem to toil after him in vain; he
talked " of Chaos carrying Noah's flood on its
back,"—likened Sir Cox Hippesley to the Witch of
Endor—and said " a motion for a Committee *would
shoulder omnipotence from the altar.*"

Mr. GRATTAN, on the other hand, immediately withdrew, and dressed himself in a full suit of black: on his return he walked up the House with a very modest gait, and looked around him with a smile of general complacency. When he rose to speak, he placed himself in a certain position, from which he did not afterwards deviate in the slightest degree, and in the utmost vehemence of his action I did not observe him to do more than to entwine, very lovingly, the two fore-fingers of the right hand with the two fore-fingers of the left. Whenever he spoke he showed his deference to the House, by treating every matter with the same degree of attention and formality, and he moved " that this Bill be read a third time to-morrow, *if then engrossed,*" with the same tone in which he defended our whole system of Finance. But in all he said there was such perfect candour and such an intimate acquaintance with his subject, so much clearness in his views, so much integrity in his propositions, so much good nature and kindness in his manner, that he seemed to receive the entire confidence of the House, and to possess the esteem equally of his adversaries and his friends.

I was much surprised to see that the next two Gentlemen who presented themselves both came from the same side of the House; but when I recognised Mr. HORNER and BROUGHAM, I felt that the arrangement was quite proper; as no two persons could be more opposed to one another in manners, character, and principles, than they, and that a union between them would be absolutely necessary to the establishing a general harmony.

The operation had scarcely been finished on these Gentlemen, when Mr. HORNER started up in the most impudent manner, and began a *lengthy*, violent, and coarse attack upon all mankind, from the Prince Regent down to Mr. Abbot, a Brewer of Canterbury. He called every body by the grossest names, and when Mr. PONSONBY rose to endeavour,

as it seemed, to moderate his fury, he lent him such
a box on the ear, as knocked the silver spectacles
which he wore on his forehead into Mr. PETER
GRANT'S right eye, and nearly prostrated the
reverend leader himself on the floor—but what
most surprised me was, the diarrha or flux of
speech which now flowed from Mr. HORNER'S lips,
and the eternal repetitions of the same thought in
all the various words and forms which the vocabu-
lary of the vulgar tongue could supply; indeed
there seemed no reason why he might not have
gone on, stringing words, like beads, on one thread,
for the whole night long; but a look of general despair, and a loud cry of question, confounded him,
and obliged him to sit down ; upon which I observed
that Lord MILTON and Mr. CHARLES WYNNE,
between whom Mr. HORNER had been before
sitting, changed their places, and Sir FRANCIS
BURDETT and Lord COCHRANE went up and shook
hands with him.

Q

Mr. BROUGHAM, on the contrary, had acquired by the change a sedate, solemn, and gentlemanly manner; he did not speak long, but he spoke well; he expressed a proper indignation against Jacobins, a manly contempt of Mountebanks, and the greatest abhorrence of bluster, quibble, evasion, and pettifogging; he picked up Mr. PONSONBY'S spectacles, and presented them to him with a compassionate smile; he endeavoured to give a kind turn to the absurdities which Mr. HORNER had uttered, and took his seat near Mr. WILLIAM ELLIOT, with whom he continued in close and friendly conversation for the rest of the evening.

The next couple that underwent the trepan were Mr. BRAGGE BATHURST and Sir JOHN NEWPORT.

Sir JOHN soon exhibited very solid marks of gravity and good sense; but spoke in so very low a tone, that I could with difficulty collect the tenor of his discourse. Those, however, who were near enough to hear, seemed by their attention and approbation to find in it a great deal of good matter and sound reasoning. In adverting to the Catholic Question, Sir JOHN became more distinct; he expressed his determination to resist those claims on every occasion, and he paid a handsome compliment to the memory of the late Doctor Duigenan; he expressed great doubts as to the propriety of the exclusive advantages lately extended to the Irish linens, and stated his determination to oppose in every stage the proposition for a grant of public money for deepening *Waterford* Harbour, which he could not but characterise as a *job;* and he sat down amidst cries of hear, hear! from Mr. HILEY ADDINGTON, Sir CHARLES POLE, and Mr. ESTCOURT.

Mr. BATHURST immediately replied to Sir JOHN, which he did in a sharp, shrill voice, and with considerable vehemence and agility: he ridiculed Mr. HILEY ADDINGTON's cheering; defended the exclusive bounty to Irish linen, and the grant to Waterford Harbour; and on the subject of the Catholic Claims, he avowed his determination never to desist from pressing that measure of strict justice and indispensable policy on the House: he largely complimented his Right Honourable Friend, the Chancellor of the Irish Exchequer; and concluded by producing a small pocket-book full of scraps of papers, out of which he gave notice of three motions —the first, for an inquiry into the Lord Chancellor's Fees; another for the Abolition of Tithes; and the third, for an account of the number of Ounces of Irish Butter consumed every morning in England and Ireland respectively, distinguishing fresh butter from salt.   Mr. BATHURST, in sitting down, placed himself between Sir HENRY PARNELL and General MATHEW.

I next thought that Mr. VESEY FITZGERALD and Mr. WILLIAM SMITH were called to the table. Mr. FITZGERALD testified great impatience, while Mr.

SMITH appeared very passive during the operation.
When it was over, Mr. FITZGERALD presented a
petition from the Society of people called Quakers,
against Church Music; and also from the three
Congregations of Dissenters, praying that all bricks
and other materials, of which conventicles are built,
might be allowed a drawback. While Mr. FITZGE-
RALD was prosing in this manner, I thought that
Mr. SMITH interrupted him with great warmth ; he
deprecated the abrogation of fiscal imposts pro-
pounded by the Right Honourable Gentleman ; he
also reprobated the assertion of his Honourable
Friend (Mr. Bankes) that Ireland had not borne
her share of taxation, and his monstrous proposition
that as the property tax was no longer wanted in
England, it should be transferred to the service
of Ireland : " Ireland," exclaimed Mr. W. SMITH,
" had sacrificed her *treasure* in the common cause,
and she was now about to sacrifice her *Treasury—*
she was even ready to part with her separate *debt,*

and to transfer to England this last proud relic of her national independence."

Mr. SMITH, every one admitted, spoke with very unusual animation and ability, and after a long and masterly speech, in which he took occasion twice to call the Speaker to order, sat down amidst loud cries of hear, hear, from Messrs. LESLIE FOSTER and CROKER.

The next exchange was between Viscounts PALMERSTONE and FOLKESTONE. Some little delay was occasioned by a strong repugnance evinced by the former to Lord FOLKESTONE's red waistcoat; but the Speaker observing that a change of *heads* did not immediately involve an interchange of *dress*, Lord PALMERSTONE acquiesced.

When the Surgeons had dismissed the Noble Members, Lord FOLKESTONE lost no time in opening a great red box, which lay at his feet, and, producing a paper therefrom, he proceeded in the clearest and most satisfactory manner to move the

Army Extraordinaries—he took occasion in the course of his speech to pay the highest compliments to the Commander-in-Chief, and to remind the House of the complete refutation which the infamous calumnies of Mrs. Clarke and her associates had now received, and he expressed his heartfelt satisfaction at being able to state, before his country, that HE had had no participation in any part of that disgusting transaction. His Lordship next entered into an animated defence of the Military Club; and concluded by expressing a hope that Mr. BANKES, or some other independent Member, would propose a vote of 1000*l.* towards defraying the outfit, first cost of plate, waiters' liveries, &c. &c. for that most useful establishment.

Lord PALMERSTONE rose to reply to the Noble Lord—" He objected—he objected to all estimates original or supplemental—or supplemental. He saw portentous signs—signs, in every street, that this— this country was on the eve of becoming a military—

a military country;—Punch—Punch, who in the days of our ancestors was accompanied—companied by a fiddle, or a—fiddle or a dulcimer, was now accompanied—companied by a drum—by a drum and fife—and fife :—every servant wore cock—cockades, and several, cocked—and several cocked-hats :—These were enormities—ormities not to be borne." His Lordship then made a violent attack upon Mr. Merryman, the Chief Clerk in the War Office, and gave notice of a motion for the release of Miss Kitty Willis, who had been last night committed to Tothill-fields Bridewell, for only wiping her face with the handkerchief of a Gentleman whom she happened to meet in the Willow-walk.

The next pair were Mr. CROKER and Mr. H. MARTIN : Mr. CROKER at first objected against having any thing to do with Mr. MARTIN's skull, which he averred never could fit his head; but the voice of the House appearing to sanction the Speaker's decision, he was obliged to submit, which he did however with a very ill grace. After the operation, as soon as Mr. CROKER had resumed his seat, he fell into a profound sleep, from which he did not awake, even while he made a very violent speech, which seemed to be directed against the memory of the late Mr. Perceval; but as the Hon. Member had totally lost his voice, as well as his sight and hearing, I was not able to collect the precise points of his harangue.

Mr. MARTIN, on the other hand, seemed wonderfully enlivened by the operation : he opened his eyes with great agility, and talked with considerable vehemence and volubility; and though he had lost but little of his own modest assurance, he seemed to have acquired something of an Irish accent. He entered into a long defence of the efficiency of his Honourable Friend Sir G. WARRENDER, as a Lay Lord of the Admiralty, and appealed to Mr. TIERNEY, as an instance of a Civilian being able to attain a most perfect and useful acquaintance with the affairs of the naval departments.

On finishing what he had to say, Mr. MARTIN immediately joined Mr. PEEL and Mr. ROBINSON* on one of the back benches, where there was a good deal of laughing, and it seemed by their gestures that Mr. MARTIN was entertaining his new companions with some ridiculous story about Sir SAMUEL ROMILLY and Sir ARTHUR PIGOTT.

The next couple which presented themselves were Mr. H. ADDINGTON and Gen. MATHEW: Mr. Cline, who operated on Gen. MATHEW, had great difficulty in getting through the operation, on account of the immense quantity of hair, and he was at last obliged to shave the head; observing with a smile, when the skull was separated, that the head appeared much better furnished on the outside than within.

As soon as the interchange had been completed, Mr. ADDINGTON rose, and in the most vehement manner denounced the Government, and more par-

* The Right Honourable Fred. Robinson, Vice-President of the Board of Trade.—E.

ticularly the Home Department, for its conduct to the Irish Catholics : he declared that there was not *one* Protestant soldier at the battle of Waterloo, and that ten-ninths of the whole of Lord Wellington's army, including the Belgians, were Irish Roman Catholics. " If that gallant people, I mean the Irish," said Mr. ADDINGTON, with great animation, " remain one week longer in their present state of torture, agony, and inconvenience, I will put myself at the head of seven millions of this suffering people who now were starving in Dyot-street, St. Giles's, and with them effect the conquest of Great Britain, and put every Protestant householder to the sword, except only those who profess Popery."

On the other hand, Gen. MATHEW, with considerable diffidence, and in a rather inaudible voice, replied to Mr. ADDINGTON : he complimented him on his great abilities, and thanked him for his candour and moderation. He said, he should feel it necessary, not only in point of *courtesy*, but as a

part of his official *duty*, to communicate his remarks
to the Noble Lord, at the head of the Home Department; to whom, the General further observed,
no complaint was ever made in vain, and whose
diligence and integrity in the discharge of his public
functions all parties were ready to acknowledge;
and he pledged himself to be able to give a most
satisfactory answer to Mr. ADDINGTON's remarks
in the course of a few—he might say, a *very* few
days.

I next observed a Gentleman, who seemed very
anxious to catch the Speaker's eye, and appeared
much mortified that he had not been considered
of sufficient consequence to be called upon before—
It was Mr. METHUEN : on his offering himself, Mr.
Speaker rose, and requested the directions of the
House, as he felt himself unequal to decide who
should be considered a fair contrast for Mr. ME-
THUEN ; who had agreed with every side by turns,
and seemed to be in determined opposition to no

one but *himself.* Upon this, methought, a long debate ensued, which ended in appointing Mr. PLUMER to change heads with Mr. METHUEN; Mr. PLUMER assuring the House that he never had changed his side or his vote, and that he had never once voted with any Government, nor ever would, whatever should be the subject, and whether he considered them wrong or right.

This preliminary being thus arranged, Messrs. METHUEN and PLUMER placed themselves in the hands of the surgeons: I observed that Mr. Cline had great difficulty in sawing off Mr. PLUMER's occiput, which seemed to be of the hardest and thickest substance; while Sir Everard Home, after feeling Mr. METHUEN's skull, laid by his instruments, and taking up a small pen-knife, divided the scalp with as much ease as if he were cutting a piece of paste-board; and, indeed, when the piece was taken off, I observed, with great surprise, that there was nothing whatsoever in the head, and that in fact it appeared in every particular like one of those *paper masks* which one sees in the shops of the Haymarket.

When the change was effected, Mr. METHUEN took his seat on the corner of the opposition bench, and stretching out his legs, crossed them upon his cane, and remained in that attitude without speaking or moving till eleven o'clock, at which hour he went away to bed.

Mr. PLUMER, on the contrary, took his seat close behind Lord CASTLEREAGH, and immediately gave notice of a motion for impeaching his Noble Friend; whom, with all due affection and regard, he would say it, he hoped to bring to the block. After a few other equally discreet observations, he was proceeding to make his motion, but it unluckily turned out that he was unable to *read* it,* and he sat down amidst shouts of laughter from all sides of the House.

* Something of this kind had occurred to Mr. Methuen.

Mr. Peregrine Courtney now rose to observe, that he thought it was very indecorous for a Gentleman holding such opinions as Mr. Plumer now professed to sit behind the Treasury Bench, and to be in a situation to overhear the conversation which might pass between Members of the Government: but Lord Castlereagh observing that though the Hon. Member might overhear such conversation, yet it was notorious he could not understand them; Mr. Plumer was, therefore, allowed to keep his place.

The Speaker next called on Mr. Peel and Lord Althorpe, who immediately advanced to the table. The operation on Mr. Peel was soon performed by Sir Everard Home, but Mr. Cline's instruments seemed to make very little impression on his Lordship's head, though he held it, with Doctor Spurzheim's assistance, tight between his knees, and though he tried all his knives and saws, one after another, it was evident he made no kind of progress.

Sir Everard Home was then called in to assist, but after a considerable delay, Mr. PEEL declared " he could wait no longer, as he found it very cold without his head;" and taking his occiput off the table, he put it on, and went to resume his seat near Mr. HENRY MARTIN. After, however, a great deal of labour, and blunting and breaking most of their instruments, the surgeons contrived to get through Lord ALTHORPE's skull: but the piece that remained in Mr. Cline's hand proved to be so unexpectedly heavy, that it escaped from his grasp, and fell upon the floor with so loud and heavy a sound, that I awoke with the noise, and to my great astonishment found myself in my own bed, up two pair of stairs backwards, in Beaufort's-buildings.

I am, Sir, your obedient Servant,

A REPORTER.

THE END.